RAIS NATURALLY

A PARENT'S GUIDE TO HERBAL MEDICINE
FROM NEWBORN TO ADOLESCENCE STEP BY STEP

AVA GREEN

Library of Congress Control Number: 2022935898

Important notice

Please note the information contained within this document is for educational and entertainment purposes only. The book is written by experienced and knowledgeable herbalism enthusiasts, not physicians. No parts of this book are meant to replace the advice of a medical professional. Do not try self-diagnosis or attempt self-treatment for serious or long-term problems without first consulting a qualified medical herbalist or medical practitioner as appropriate. Do not take any herb without first referring to the safety sections and always check with your physician. Do not exceed any dosages recommended. Always consult a professional practitioner if symptoms persist. If taking prescribed medicines, seek professional medical advice before using herbal remedies. Take care to correctly identify plants and do not harvest restricted or banned species. The Publisher and the author make no representations or warranties with respect to the accuracy or completeness of the contents of this work and specifically disclaim all warranties, including without limitation warranties of fitness for a particular purpose.

Practice, laws, and regulations all change, and the reader should obtain up-to-date professional advice on any such issues. You should research your local laws before using the information in this book. The authors and the publisher expressly disclaim any liability, loss, or risk, personal or otherwise, which is incurred as a consequence, directly or indirectly, of the use and application of any of the contents of this book.

The authors are not your healthcare providers. This book is a beginner-friendly guide, free of heavy and complex terminology, offering a simple and step-by-step approach to herbalism.

This book provides content related to physical and/or mental health issues. As such, use of this book implies your acceptance of this disclaimer.

Special Bonus!

Join Our FB group to find new herbal recipes and to share experiences with your new herbal friends!

Scan this QR code below to get the LINK to our FB group! See you there!

www.theherb.space/group

Contents

Special Bonus!

Join Our FB group to find new herbal recipes and to share experiences with your new herbal friends!

Scan this QR code below to get the LINK to our FB group! See you there!

www.theherb.space/group

Contents

Introduction

Are you doing everything you can to keep your baby healthy?

Of course you want to! But it's not always easy to know how. There are many ways to make sure your baby is happy and healthy, and grows into an equally happy and healthy young person. This book is to introduce you to my favorite way of keeping my family healthy – by using the amazing medicinal herbal gifts that mother nature provides for us.

A few years ago, a large baby food corporation had to recall its product due to the presence of unacceptable levels of lead. Another large corporation had to recall its baby powder for the presence of asbestos that was linked to an increased risk of cancer. It is not uncommon for companies to recall foods, lotions, bath products, and other supposedly "child safe" products for having high levels of lead, arsenic, asbestos, or other heavy metals (Kuzemchak, 2021). Parents are often shocked to find that the product they thought would be great for their child is, in reality, dangerous and toxic. Each year, a list of baby products recalled by the FDA is made available to the public so that parents can keep track of these unacceptable items. It doesn't have to be this way.

Our children deserve only the best we have to offer. When you become a parent, you begin to understand this on a deeper level. The need to provide the best for your child becomes more and more clear. In a world full of product recalls, toxic ingredients, and deceptive marketing claims, parents have to be informed and educated about how to provide their children with the best in terms of their health and wellbeing.

Sometimes, as new or even experienced parents, it's hard to know what to expect during your child's development, what to be worried about, and what is safe in the line of modern medicine. One of the best ways to nurture your own peace of mind and your child's health is with the knowledge of herbs. There is a shortage of accurate information available about the use of herbs for children, which is why I wanted to write this book. Also, there are those who don't have access to affordable allopathic medicine with which to treat their child's ailments. Herbs and other medicinal plants can truly help those who don't otherwise have the help they need.

One of my lifelong best friends, Sarah, lives in an area where there are not many good doctors and those who are there are terribly expensive. She often rings me up to ask advice about her health or that of her spouse or children, and I am always happy to help because they deserve access to this knowledge. My grandfather, William, always told us that, although the government-run society is important and has its place, the officials are only people and, one day, things may get bad (as they have so many times throughout history) so we should learn to take care of our own communities as best we can. With everything going on in the world today, it is important to be as self-reliant as possible.

I grew up surrounded by the wonders of the natural world, always wide-eyed and learning from my family about the holistic properties of herbs and other medicinal plants. My grandmother's garden wonderland seemed huge to me when I was a small child (and in reality it was actually pretty big, when I think about it) and I loved getting lost among the rows and rows of colorful and aromatic plants. Her expertise came from her parents and their parents before them. It's a truly remarkable journey to this point. As a parent, I have raised my children in the same manner, teaching them alongside me so that they could one day treat and teach their children as well. And they have continued the tradition with their children. It has been amazing to see this timeless knowledge passed on and to continue the legacy.

This book was designed for those who want to take a more holistic, natural approach to treating their children's various ailments. Over the years, I have become part of a huge and wonderful community of people who turn to nature, whenever possible, to cure what ails them. I have passionately devoured any source of knowledge I can find. I have learned so much through my family's lessons and my own trials and errors. I grow and use all my herbs myself because I love being a part of the process from start to finish.

This knowledge has been revolutionary for me and I want to share it with you. You will be able to use common herbs to help treat everything from diaper rash to an upset stomach. Through this book, you will have the opportunity to learn about why herbs are a safe and effective way to tackle a variety of issues you may face as a parent. You will learn how herbs work in the body and how they compare with commercial products. By understanding how herbs work and how to use them yourself, you will be able to feel more confident about working with herbs and creating herbal formulations for your children and family. There is no greater feeling as a parent than knowing you are able to treat your child with the best, safest and purest formulations available.

From the moment our children come into this world, they have needs. This book will help you navigate these needs as they arise. It has been divided into sections to make it easier for you to use. You will be able to read about important milestones in your child's life, from the moment he or she enters this world, as well as about the ways you can help support your child, naturally, during these stages. You will be walked through the first year of a child's life and provided with gentle yet powerful remedies that you can use to make your baby more comfortable as he or she grows and encounters new challenges. (By the way, in this book I talk about the genders of babies interchangeably. Please replace the gender with what is appropriate for your baby.)

The book begins with your child's first moments and what you can expect at this time, then transitions to your child's first five days. The first five days are crucial as both of you are getting to know each other. Next, you will be able to read about your child's first month of life, and access tools and strategies to help you nurture and give support during this time. From there, you will be able to read about remedies for months two through four. It's during these months that parents may need help with issues like colic and reflux. Months four through six will cover issues such as dietary supplements, teething, sleep, and dental care. It won't be long before your little one will learn to walk, so months six through nine will tackle remedies for any bumps and bruises that may arise. Months nine through twelve will follow, with highly beneficial remedies for soothing tantrums and treating ear infections.

The first year of your child's life isn't all this book covers. You will be able to learn about stages in your child's life all the way through to the adult years. Each stage brings with it new obstacles, but you can rest assured that you will be ready for whatever comes, using the wisdom and knowledge you gain from this book. From childhood cuts and scrapes to acne during adolescence, you will have the tools you need to provide your child with the appropriate support. All of the precious herbal remedies in this book can be used to keep your child comfortable and happy as he or she thrives under the umbrella of your love. Even if you already have children, each child is different and

so a new baby always brings a whole new experience. The joy of herbs is that they aren't a 'one size fits all' type of treatment; they can be adjusted for each child.

Over the years many of my family and friends have come to me for assistance in finding an herbal remedy for an ailment. Then, once their ailment passes, they've come back and thanked me for all they have learned about herbal remedies. Even families that have to work multiple jobs have been able to treat their kids in natural ways because of the knowledge I have provided them. I am now happily able to provide this knowledge to you as well.

It can be frustrating, as a parent, when you buy books and they don't cover remedies to treat common childhood issues. I read many books each time I was pregnant, in anticipation of my new baby. None covered what I needed to know and none offered holistic treatments. This book was designed to cover issues that real parents deal with each day, like ear infections, sleep trouble, croup, viruses, immune system nourishment, rashes, allergies, anxiety, constipation, coughs, attention deficit hyperactivity disorder (ADHD), and even remedies to help children with special needs. No more frustration and disappointment at not finding the help you need.

Not only that, but the remedies detailed in this book are for all parents, regardless of their experience with herbs. The novice and experienced parent alike can benefit from this information. There is no need to fret over a long list of herbs for each remedy, either. These remedies are effective yet simple and easy to create. They will not require you to find a stack of different herbs with which to create a single remedy. This will give you time to take care of your little one while also having time to create useful remedies for them. With the remedies in this book, it is possible to do both!

Parenting can be very overwhelming. You may feel as though you are learning as you go, and that's because you are. No one is born knowing how to parent, in fact, there are probably more parenting philosophies than stars in the sky. You may even feel that you aren't capable of handling the challenges when they arise. We all feel this way sometimes, but just know that you are not alone! Consider this book your resource and friend as you encounter the trials of parenthood.

With the guidance given here, you will be able to confront whatever comes your way and feel more empowered as you overcome each challenge. If you are expecting, read about protocols you can have in place so you can be ready for your baby's entrance into this world, as well as for your little one's first month of life. As your child grows, and this will happen very quickly, keep following along and reading ahead so you have an idea of what to expect at each stage. You will be more than ready to treat any issues that may arise.

Why do you think parents are turning to herbs? Start the next chapter and find out. Take a deep breath. You've got this!

Why Moms and Dads Are Turning to Herbalism

Apart from the fact that many commercially produced baby products have to be recalled each year due to safety concerns, there are loads of other reasons why moms and dads are turning to herbs for treating their children's common ailments. Herbs have been used for thousands of years to treat numerous conditions. Thousands of years of successful use with children is certainly a very reassuring recommendation for parents concerned with safety.

Many commercial wellness products for children contain unsavory ingredients like parabens, bisphenol A, phthalates, petroleum by-products, sulfates, alcohols, and endocrine disrupting chemicals. Some of these ingredients are absorbed through the skin and into the body. As humans, our skin is our biggest organ and our first line of defense against the external world. Skin absorbs the things it comes into contact with on a daily basis, including lotions, body washes, and creams. A child's skin is even more sensitive and absorbent. The effects that these ingredients will have on children in the long run are unknown, but it is thought they may be partially responsible for the increase in chronic childhood illnesses, such as autoimmune disease, cancer, and hormonal issues seen in children today.

Bisphenol A is often used in plastic packaging. We seldom give much thought to the containers we used to store children's lotions, and creams. But the fact is that many plastic containers have this substance in them and it can leach into the product itself, especially if the product is exposed to heat of any kind. When using herbal remedies you make at home, you get to pick the containers and can choose something made of glass or wood, for example, that doesn't contain bisphenol A. When you make your own herbal remedies, you don't have to worry about the presence of endocrine disrupting chemicals like those added to baby products to give them fragrance. Synthetic fragrance is one of the worst offenders when it comes to endocrine disruption, allergies, and carcinogens. When you make your own herbal products at home, you don't add any synthetic fragrances so there's no need to fret about what toxic substances your child may be exposed to. The natural

fragrances of the herbs you use are all you need, and I personally love them a million times more than the artificial stuff.

In addition to synthetic fragrances in commercial baby products, many also contain synthetic dyes to give the product a bright color. These colors may seem fun and make the product look cute, but dyes are made using toxic ingredients that have been linked to behavioral disorders, tumors, and allergies. The artificial colorants can cause children to break out in rashes when they are exposed to these products. Using the remedies in this book, you will be able to create pure, all-natural products that you can use with confidence on your children without worrying about these reactions. Many herbs and other plants can be used to dye products naturally. If you get into that particular bit of herbalism, you'll find a fascinating and fun world of color.

When you know more about the unnecessary and potentially dangerous ingredients hiding in many commercial products, you begin to understand why it's so important to give your child the very best. This is especially true in this world of misleading marketing and unrealistic claims where your child may end up paying the price. When you make your own herbal remedies, you know exactly what ingredients are present and won't be in for any nasty surprises.

Parents naturally want to give their children remedies that work well, but skip the toxic ingredients. That is another reason why herbs are amazing to use for everyday ailments. They have been used for centuries to treat all kinds of issues, ranging from rashes to respiratory complaints. They work just as well as many commercial products, and sometimes even better, because they come without the nasty side-effects that many over-the-counter remedies can have.

For example, if your child has a fever and you want to reduce it, you can go to your local drug store and buy a common pain reliever/fever reducer. But did you know that products that contain acetaminophen actually deplete glutathione levels? Glutathione is an important antioxidant our body's need to combat illness, mop up free radicals, and even cope with heavy metal exposure. Depleting these levels in your sick child only makes it harder for him or her to fight off the cause of the fever.

Also, fevers are nature's way of getting rid of the body's sickness. The immune system raises the body's temperature to create an environment inhospitable to the virus or bacteria; therefore, it is not necessary to worry about a fever unless it is dangerously high or continues for a prolonged period. Fever reducers only treat a symptom, not the actual causative agent, and may even interfere with the body's natural defenses. Aside from this, many commercial fever reducers for children contain scary levels of sugar and red dye (which may contain contaminants that are known cancer causing substances). There are gentle, yet effective herbal remedies for reducing your child's fever that help to nourish and strengthen the immune system at the same time, which is what a child really needs when ill.

Parents are also turning to herbs because they can treat such a wide range of ailments. It can be difficult to go to the store and buy remedies that work for an assortment of issues, from ear infections to behavioral issues. But with herbs, you can create remedies that tackle these issues, and more, without ever leaving your home. This empowers parents who may previously have felt helpless to support their children when they were sick.

When your child is happy and healthy, you are happy and healthy! We have all been in a position where we are miserable because our children are miserable, but herbs help make it possible to give them comfort, peace, and assistance while simultaneously helping us feel better. Our bodies respond to stress in a negative way by creating cortisol and other harmful hormones. Long term, this can lead to health issues like high blood pressure, as well as increasing levels of anxiety and stress. As parents, we already have our hands full and we don't need more stress in our lives. Herbal remedies give us repose as they give our children relief. This results in a happier, more peaceful home environment.

But Wait, Is This Safe?

Herbs have a long history of use on every continent, from Indian Ayurvedic Medicine and Traditional Chinese Medicine to Native American and Indigenous use of herbs. Some of these herbal medicine traditions date back as far as the 11th century BCE. This is what has been documented, but the use of herbs for treating illness likely dates back to the dawn of humankind. Archeologists have actually uncovered evidence that early man may have been using plants like yarrow (*Achillea millefolium*) as far back as 60,000 years ago (Lakshmi et al., 2011).

Even with all this history of use, some people are still skeptical when it comes to the safety of herbs. One reason for this is the advent of modern allopathic medicine (a system where doctors and nurses treat illnesses and diseases) around 200 years ago. Since this time, more and more people have relied on this form of medicine to treat illness. As a result, they are unfamiliar with herbal medicine traditions, usage, and safety. Keep in mind that the modern allopathic model of medicine many utilize today has only been around a short period when you look at the broad timeline of history. Allopathic medicine is relatively new and we are only now beginning to learn about the serious side effects associated with many drugs and pharmaceuticals. The list of potential side effects for almost any allopathic drug is long and may even include death (how scary is that?). Contrary to what many may believe, herbs are an infinitely safer choice.

Herbal and modern allopathic medicine do have something in common. Many common, over-the-counter and prescribed pharmaceuticals are derived from herbs. Even today, plants are needed in order to develop many drugs. The medicinal compounds are often extracted from plants in a lab and then chemically altered to make the drug. Although this process creates a strong drug, it also creates something with strong side effects. Some common examples of drugs derived from medicinal plants today include Ibuprofen and products containing aspirin. Aspirin is created using a compound called salicin that is most often taken from the bark of white willow trees (*Salix alba*). Long before scientists were able to take this compound and turn it into aspirin, early man was infusing white willow bark in water to make a pain-relieving and fever-reducing tea (without the harmful effects on the kidneys that aspirin may have). This particular treatment is one well known and used in my household, particularly for my husband and his back.

Another example of this is star anise (*Illicium verum*), which contains a compound called shikimic acid. Shikimic acid was extracted in a lab and used to create a popular antiviral influenza treatment called Tamiflu. Poppies (*Papaver somniferum*) are used to make codeine, which is still used today in cough syrup and pain medicine. In addition, foxglove (*Digitalis purpurea*) is used to create a heart medication to treat congestive heart failure. The list is long when it comes to plants used to create pharmaceuticals today. However, all of these pharmaceuticals come with a lengthy list of side effects and can be extremely dangerous to some people, especially if the medicines are taken in the wrong dosages. On the other hand, herbs can provide a safe alternative to lab-created pharmaceuticals because their active constituents aren't chemically altered. Herbs are gentle and work with the body instead of against it.

Herbs are very different from pharmaceuticals because they are made using the whole plant rather than just the active compound that has been altered in a lab. By using the active compound exclusively, modern drugs have lost all benefits that may come from other compounds in the plant. We forget that all compounds that make up a plant are there for a reason. Plants offer a unique opportunity for healing the body because they can target the affected areas, while also benefiting other parts of the body. This is in stark contrast to modern drugs, which target areas to heal, but potentially harm other areas in the process.

Another reason that herbs make a much safer choice for healing is that they help to target the root cause. Think of it this way: if you had a gaping wound, would you slap a bandage on it to soak up the blood or would you try to clean the wound and put it back together first? This is similar to what is happening today with many modern drugs. They are a "bandage" to cover up a potentially serious problem.

Targeting the actual root cause is the only way to ensure true healing. If you have any experience with modern allopathic medicine at all, you may have found that most pharmaceuticals treat the *symptoms* of the issue and not the root cause, as I described above for fevers. For example, there is a wide array of pharmaceuticals available for treating pain but most of them don't address the cause of the pain. What is being done to treat the root cause? Oftentimes, not much. Furthermore, the proliferation of different pain relief medications has created a crisis because some of these substances are addictive. Many people have died or become enslaved to a regimen of constant pharmaceutical use to treat various symptoms or even side effects of other prescription medicines. Since the root cause is never targeted, the problem goes on and on and becomes a chronic issue that can result in a lower quality of life.

Herbal remedies target the root cause of an issue so a person can experience *true* healing. For example, if you are suffering from pain caused by a sore throat, you can take pain medication or you can try gargling with an herbal blend of sage and ginger. These herbs provide relief while also targeting inflammation, spasmodic coughing, and any bacteria in the area. Less coughing means less irritation and inflammation in the throat. The antimicrobial compounds in the herbal blend kill harmful bacteria that may be causing inflammation and pain. Instead of masking the pain, you can use herbs that actually target the real problem at its root.

Herbs to Avoid

While herbs are a truly remarkable and natural gift to us, there are some that you will want to avoid or use with extreme caution when it comes to children. Cora Collette Breuner, MD, MPH, FAAP, professor of Pediatrics and Adolescent Medicine and adjunct professor of Orthopedics and Sports Medicine at Seattle Children's Hospital and the University of Washington, Seattle, lists the following as precautionary: licorice (*Glycyrrhiza glabra*), ephedra (*Ephedra equisetina* Bge.), aconite, Dutchman's pipe (*Aristolochia*), deadly nightshade (*Atropa belladonna*), blue cohosh (*Caulophyllum thalictroides*), borage (*Borago officinalis*), Scotch broom (*Cytisus scoparius*), sweet flag (*Acorus calamus*), chaparral (*Larrea tridentata*), coltsfoot (*Tussilago farfara*), comfrey (*Symphytum officinale*), germander (*Teucrium chamaedrys*), life root (*Senecio aureus*), lobelia, pennyroyal (*Mentha pulegium*), poke root (*Phytolacca americana*), sassafras (*Sassafras albidum*), skullcap (*Scutellaria lateriflora*), tansy ragwort (*Jacobaea vulgaris*), and wormwood (*Artemisia absinthium*) (Zimlich, 2017).

According to Bruener, supplements that require extra caution and that should be discontinued prior to surgery include echinacea (*Echinacea purpurea*), ephedra (*Ephedra equisetina* Bge.), garlic (*Allium sativum*), gingko (*Gingko biloba*), ginseng (*Panax ginseng, P. quinquefolius, P. repens*), kava (*Piper methysticum*), St. John's wort (*Hypericum perforatum*), and valerian (*Valeriana officinalis*).

Herbs such as arnica (*Arnica montana*) and comfrey (*Symphytum officinale*) are only to be used externally. Uva ursi (*Arctostaphylos uva-ursi*), mistletoe (*Phoradendron serotinum*), and buckthorn (*Frangula purshiana*) should also be avoided. Some of these herbs have prescription drug interactions, others are too strong for use in children, and some alter hormone levels. It is best to avoid using these herbs when treating children.

DO NOT's

Common sense and knowledge are key to the safe use of herbs. Your job as a parent is to keep your children safe. Never inject anything you make into your or your child's body. That's not how herbal remedies work. For internal treatments, safe herbs that have been infused into oils are perfectly okay to ingest, but oils infused with herbs such as chaparral (*Larrea tridentata*), arnica (*Arnica montana*), comfrey (*Symphytum officinale*), and ma-huang (*Ephedra sinica*) should not be given to your children (and use extreme caution should you decide to take them internally yourself). Always research any herbs before taking or administering them if you or your child is on a prescription medication or aspirin. Research carefully before taking herbs when pregnant, breastfeeding, or before surgery.

Check Allergy with the Scratch Test

Try performing a "scratch test" with an herb you plan on using with your child before administering the herbal preparation. This will help you establish whether or not your child is allergic to the particular herb. Take a small amount of the preparation and rub some on the inside of the child's arm. Wait twenty-four hours to see if there is a reaction.

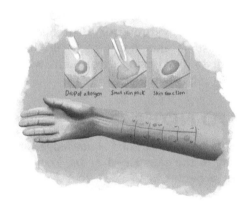

Always research the herbs you plan on using to make sure they are safe for use with children.

- Gentle herbs that are often used with children include oats (*Avena sativa*), nettle (*Urtica dioica*), agrimony (*Agrimonia eupatoria*),

rose hips (*Rosa canina*), dandelion (*Taraxacum officinale*), violet (*Viola* spp.), red raspberry (*Rubus idaeus*), alfalfa (*Medicago sativa*), marshmallow (*Althaea officinalis*), lemon balm (*Melissa officinalis*), catnip (*Nepeta cataria*), lavender (*Lavandula angustifolia*), spearmint (*Mentha spicata*), elder flowers and berries (*Sambucus* spp.), mullein (*Verbascum thapsus*), yarrow (*Achillea millefolium*), and slippery elm (*Ulmus rubra*). That said, make sure you test the herbs with the scratch test (one herb at a time) before administering any of them.

- While chamomile (*Matricaria recutita* and *Anthemis nobilis*) is generally safe for many children, it can trigger an allergic reaction in some. Echinacea (*Echinacea angustifolia*) can also cause allergic reactions. With these herbs it is especially important to perform a scratch test with these before administering to make sure they do not cause allergic reactions.

Dosages

When it comes to the safety of herbs for children, dosages are important. Although herbs are generally safe, keep in mind that a child doesn't need the same amount of an herbal remedy as an adult would receive. Like with any other drug, children need much smaller doses. There are several things to keep in mind as you determine a suitable dosage for your child:

- In general, most herbal formulations require doses meant for an adult of around 150 to 200 pounds (68 kg). Of course, children

are much smaller and so require lower doses.

- Tinctures and extracts are stronger than other herbal preparations and require much lower doses than other remedies. They shouldn't be administered to a child who is less than one year of age. Solvent-based extractions like these often require one drop for every pound (0.5 kg) of a child's body weight. It is a good idea to start off with the lowest recommended dosage and wait three hours before repeating this dosage (if needed).

- You can also practice "titrating" doses. This involves treating initially with the smallest recommended dosage and then increasing the dose, little by little, until you achieve the desired results (without going above the highest recommended dose). There isn't a formal method for titrating, when it comes to children. Keep in mind that each herb is different and the dose present in each type of remedy can vary depending on many factors, such as when the herbs were harvested (this can affect potency), the type of herb being used, and the way in which the remedy itself is prepared. It is also important to take the condition of the unwell child into consideration, whether urgent treatment is necessary or not.

Is it acute? Does your child seem to respond to the remedy at the dose currently being administered? If the situation is more acute, such as when your child is up throughout the night, with congestion, you might consider using a stronger

herbal formulation and titrating the dosage rapidly until they feel better. If it isn't an acute situation, you might consider starting off with a weaker formulation (like a tea) and administering as needed.

- Some herbalists recommend calculating the dosage for a child by taking his or her age and adding 12 to it and then dividing the child's age by this number. This is referred to as "Young's Rule." An example would be: 7 (age)+12 = 19, then 7/19 = 0.38, and approximate that to 1/3 of an adult dose. "Clark's Rule" is another rule for calculating dosage and involves taking a child's weight in pounds, and dividing by 150. For example, for a child whose weight is 40lbs the calculation would be: 40/150 = 0.27, which is just above 1/4 so you'd use 1/4 of the adult dose. As there can be a wide range of body weights in children of the same age, it is preferable to calculate an appropriate dosage using Clark's Rule.

- Whenever possible, reach for the least invasive treatment first. These include treatments a child doesn't ingest, such as a salve that is used topically. Topical applications are always safer than anything that can be taken internally. For example, if your child has congestion but the situation isn't acute, you could always administer a chest rub before bed rather than giving a strong tincture.

- Always start by using formulations that utilize only one herb and not a blend, until you are well educated on their use, as they make it harder to determine which herb is the cause of a reaction, in the case of an adverse event.

- Always research any potential side effects with each new herb you administer; this will help you to understand better the potential adverse reactions that could occur.

Another effective and non-invasive remedy would be an herbal bath or steam. For respiratory ailments, consider administering an herbal bath or steam first.

- You can add peppermint (*Mentha × piperita*) or spearmint leaves to a warm bath, in a muslin drawstring bag, and then sit with your child in the tub. The herbs infuse in the water and allow the child to inhale their gentle vapors as the warmth helps to relieve congestion. Shut the door to the bathroom and draw the bath curtain, to trap in any steam from the herbal bath.

- Another option is to make herbal steam using the shower. Hang a bundle of eucalyptus leaves from the shower and turn the hot water on. Shut the bathroom door and sit in the bathroom (not in the shower) with your child to inhale the steam. This can help to relieve congestion and coughing, and make it easier

for the child to breathe. This is especially helpful, right before bedtime, to loosen up phlegm.

- Essential oils can be used instead of the actual herbs as well, if that is what you have available. I often use peppermint and eucalyptus or rosemary essential oils in the bath for my youngest daughter, if she is congested. Here, it is important to calculate an appropriate dose first, as the ingredients in essential oils can be absorbed through the skin. I also put essential oils in our diffuser by our bed at night so my daughter can breathe them in while sleeping, making her night's sleep much more restful (as well as my own).

Following the proper dosage and safety protocols significantly reduces the likelihood that your child will have a negative experience with herbal remedies. Herbs are wonderfully safe and effective when used correctly with children, as well as with adults! The next time you find yourself wondering if an herbal remedy is safe, remember that many of us have been conditioned to rely on pharmaceuticals when, in reality, it is the pharmaceuticals that are often dangerous and come with undesirable side effects.

As wonderful as herbs are, seeking out professional doctors and allopathic medicine absolutely has its time and place. Unfortunately, holistic medicine won't fix everything and sometimes things like antibiotics, insulin, and cancer treatments are needed and must be used. Holistic and allopathic medicines are very important pieces in the puzzle of health that is influenced by many different elements, including psychology, biology, genetics, environmental aspects and parenting methods.

Some instances where professional medical help should be sought immediately include deep wounds (cuts, punctures, etc), head injuries, broken bones, suspected internal bleeding (often shows up as large bruises in organ rich areas), serious accidents, life threatening allergic reactions, seizures, and stubborn symptoms that don't improve within a few days (as this may indicate a need for antibiotics). As you know, genes, environment, parenting styles and mindsets, and just about everything else can have a considerable impact on your child; it's all a complicated puzzle. Herbs are just a piece of this puzzle, and they can't fix EVERY problem. So please do your own research and when in doubt, seek out professional advice. Try to find an allopathic provider who supports your use of herbal remedies. Finding one with the same values makes your life much easier.

Harnessing the Essence of Herbs

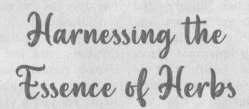

Whether you are just getting started with herbs or have been using them for years, there are many ways in which you can find and harness the essence of these amazing and beneficial plants. Using herbs doesn't have to be complicated at all. Learning the basics will give you a good idea of how to get started with herbs and the various ways in which you can use them.

Finding Your Herbs

First things first. Where on earth do you find the herbs to use for all the wonderful remedies I'm going to teach you about? There are a few different ways to access your herbs.

1. Growing
2. Foraging
3. Buying

1. Personally, **growing** my own herbs to use is my absolute favorite and most fulfilling way. There is nothing quite like being a part of the process from the very beginning, and watching a small seed turn

into a fully fledged remedy for what ails me or my family and friends. The routine of tending to the plants and nurturing their growth is very relaxing for me and gives me a chance to slow down in this crazy, fast-paced world. I go into the growing process in depth in my book *Grow Your Own Medicine*. Check it out for yourself and see if growing your own herbs might interest you.

2. **Foraging** is a particularly fun way to get medicinal plants because mother nature really provides us with a great deal of bounty. Some of my favorite local herbs are goldenrod, plantain (both broad and narrow leaf varieties), clover, mullein, pine, juniper, usnea, poke, and nettle. Most of these are in my own back yard. It is very important to educate yourself well before foraging because some plants have toxic lookalikes. There are many resources out there, including field guides, to help you learn what is available in your area, how to identify it correctly, when is the best time to harvest, and how best to do it.

3. **Buying** is the simplest and quickest way to get your herbs. I often utilize this method for herbs I can't grow in my zone, or during winter months when growing has slowed or stopped and the weather is unfavorable for foraging (I am not a big fan of cold weather at all). The most important part of buying is finding a reputable seller. Some grow their own herbs, and some forage (make sure they are ethically sourced). Our facebook group, Herbalism For Beginners

At Home – Medicinal Herbs and Herbalist Remedies, is a great place to find recommendations on the best places to buy herbs.

Your Herbal Formulations

To avoid repeating this for every recipe in this book, refer back to this chapter when needed. In this book we will not go into the nitty gritty details of what the active compounds and constituents of herbs are and how they affect your body. For that you can read *The Art of Herbal Healing: Herbalism for Beginners*. Alright, here we go ...

Macerated Oils

Macerated oils (commonly known as oil infusions) are very handy for topical use. They can be used by themselves or combined with other ingredients to make a salve (see salve recipe below). Herbal oil infusions should always be made using dried herbs because any water content in plants can cause the oils to go rancid.

There are two main ways to make an herbal oil infusion:

A. The Traditional Method

1. Fill a sterile jar with dried plant material.

2. Completely cover it with a carrier oil. Carrier oils are plant oils used as a base in a product. Some great carrier oils include olive oil, jojoba, avocado, sweet almond, rosehip, coconut, hemp seed, apricot kernel, and grapeseed oils. Each carrier oil has its own unique skin-healing properties as well as a specific shelf life, so research which carrier oil would be best for your specific needs, before creating an herbal oil infusion.

3. Put the lid on and let it infuse. Some people prefer letting the heat from the sun infuse their oil, and heat does a great job at this. However, sunlight also damages the integrity of herbs and their potency. To avoid this, you can put your jar in a brown paper bag and leave it on a windowsill that gets sunlight, or outside in an area with full sun.

4. Shake your jar daily to help it infuse better. You may notice that the plant material has soaked up the oil after a day or two of infusion and the amount of oil is reduced.

5. If you need to, you can top up the jar to make sure no plant material is above the oil line.

6. Let this infuse in the jar for four to six weeks before straining it out through a strainer or cheesecloth.

7. Bottle your herbal oil infusion in a tinted glass bottle or jar and store it in a cool, dark place.

B. Quick Heat Method (using a stove or crockpot)

1. To get started, fill your sterile glass jar with plant material.

2. Cover it with the carrier oil of your choice, as described above.

3. Next, sit your jar in a water bath (make sure the water isn't so high that it gets into the jar), inside a pan on the "warm" or low setting on your stovetop. Too much heat can destroy precious healing properties in the herbs, so make sure you keep the temperature on low at all times during this process.

4. Leave this for as long as you can to ensure that the heat helps the infusion process along. Let the infusion process last anywhere from eight to twelve hours. When I do oil infusions this way, I most often infuse all day; I turn it off at night so the water doesn't run low, and then turn it back on the following day. Making an infusion in this way can be very rewarding. You can follow the same procedure when using a crockpot. Keep an eye on the water level so it stays at the appropriate amount.

5. When the allotted time has passed, simply strain your oil infusion through a strainer or cheesecloth and bottle the liquid.

6. Store it in a cool, dark place to use when you need it.

All oil infusions last as long as the expiration date on the bottle of carrier oil you used, so make a note of this and label your bottle with the name of the herb infusion and the date it was created, as well as the date it will expire.

Salves

The base of an herbal salve is an herbal oil infusion. Once you create this, you can either use it on its own to apply topically, or you can combine it with beeswax to make a salve. A salve has a thicker consistency than an oil infusion, which makes it easier to apply and means it will stay in place. As a general rule, you can create a salve by combining:

- eight ounces (230 g) of an herb-infused oil
- one ounce (30 g) of beeswax

This needs to be done in a double boiler to avoid damaging the integrity of the beeswax (which has medicinal properties of its own).

Using beeswax pellets makes it much easier when it comes to melting the beeswax in the double boiler. Here's how:

1. Measure out one ounce (30 g) of beeswax pellets.

2. Add this to a double boiler on low to medium heat.

3. When the pellets are fully melted, add eight ounces (230 g) of your herb-infused oil.

4. Blend this well by stirring gently.

5. Remove your double boiler from the heat.

6. Pour your salve into jars to cool. Use either glass or tin jars with lids.

7. It will take a few hours for the salve to begin to harden and take on a thicker consistency.

8. To speed this process up, you can place your jars carefully in the refrigerator.

9. Once cooled, place a lid on each container and store in a cool, dry place.

For beginners, there is an easy way to make a salve that doesn't involve beeswax. You can use coconut oil. Coconut oil is naturally solid at room temperature, unlike most other carrier oils, although it will melt if the room temperature increases above 76°F (24°C). Note that there is also coconut oil that stays liquid; it is referred to as fractionated coconut oil. The lauric acid has been removed from fractionated coconut oil, which also means the oil doesn't offer the health benefits of that particular acid. For this reason, the solid oil is preferred. Simply substitute for beeswax in the recipe above and let the mixture solidify. Use as you would a regular salve, but keep the preparation in the refrigerator if your summer temperatures are high.

Teas

Teas are a gentle, yet effective (and most often delicious) way to create a medicinal wash or drink with herbs. It is one of my and my family's absolute favorite ways to ingest herbs. Teas can serve multiple purposes, ranging from drinking to washing wounds or even freezing to make herbal popsicles. Tea blends are one of my herbalist passions. There are so many blends you can make for a variety of ailments. And there are several ways you can infuse herbs in the water to make tea. Some popular methods include a stainless steel mesh ball that can be filled with herbs and dropped in the cup to infuse. Alternatively, you can find reusable or disposable tea bags for making your own herbal teas.

1. Place herbs in an infuser. With most herbs, you need only use one to two teaspoons of dried or fresh herb to infuse in a cup of hot water, but it does depend on the size of the herb you are infusing. For ground or finely chopped herbs, less is needed than for roughly chopped or whole herbs, such as flower heads. I often use up to a tablespoon of herb per cup because I also like a stronger flavor.

2. Add water that has been brought to a full boil.

3. For a mild tea, let it infuse for five minutes. For a somewhat stronger tea, let it infuse for ten minutes. For a strong tea, let it infuse for fifteen or more minutes.

Another method of making tea involves solar infusion, which is made by harnessing the power of the sun and allowing it to heat the herbs and infuse them into the water. One of the best times to make these infusions is during the summer solstice, when the days are longer and the sun shines brighter to help bring warmth and heat to your solar infusion.

1. Start by placing two tablespoons of the dried herb in a quart-sized Mason jar. You can add slices of cucumber, lemon, or any fruits you desire at this time as well.

2. Fill the jar with water and place it in a warm, sunny area for three hours.

3. Strain it when you bring it inside, and then enjoy it. You can add raw honey to make it more palatable, especially if you will give it to a child to drink. (Honey is not recommended for children under a year old, however, as there is a risk of botulism.) Of course, there is no need to add fruit or honey if you plan on using it as a wound wash or adding it to a sitz bath.

Tinctures

Tinctures are best used by adolescents or adults as they are much stronger extracts that are and generally don't taste as nice as other herbal formulations. They are typically added to a drink to increase its palatability. That said, tinctures are one of the best ways to process herbs because they have the longest shelf life. In addition the alcohol used to make the tincture is an excellent solvent and does a great job of pulling medicinal compounds from the plant material.

1. Fill a sterile glass jar with your dried or fresh plant material. It helps to use tinted glass to protect your tinctures from potentially harmful UV rays that break down the integrity of your medicine.

2. Completely cover herbs with ethyl alcohol that is at least 80 proof (40% alcohol by volume).

3. Sit this in a cool, dark place to infuse for four to six weeks and shake your jar daily to help aid infusion.

4. You might notice, after the first twenty-four hours, that the liquid level is lower. If any plant material is sticking up from the liquid line, simply top the jar up with more alcohol.

5. After four to six weeks, strain your tincture through a cheesecloth or strainer and bottle the liquid in a tinted dropper bottle.

6. Tincture dosages vary, but many call for one to three droppers full (Depends on baby's weight, see the dosages section in chapter "But Wait, is it safe?") up to three times daily. Dosages depend on the herbs used and the issue being addressed.

7. Tinctures can last anywhere from five to ten years, and sometimes longer, if they are stored in the refrigerator.

Tinctures all utilize alcohol as a solvent, and some people may not be comfortable with this. Although alcohol is one of the best solvents, other solvents can be used instead. An acetum is an extract that is made using vinegar as a solvent; it will taste strongly of vinegar. To make this more palatable, you can add one part raw honey for every two parts of vinegar (e.g., apple cider vinegar) you use. This creates what is referred to as an "oxymel." Alcohol can also be substituted with glycerine, to form an extract known as a glycerite, as described below.

Glycerite: A glycerite is one of the best ways to make an extract for a child or for those who abstain from alcohol. Glycerites are beloved by children because they taste excellent, yet they create a strong infusion to take medicinally. They are made using non–GMO vegetable glycerin and a little water.

1. Fill a clean glass jar with chopped plant material.

a. If you are using dried material, you need only fill the jar halfway. If you are using fresh plant material, fill the jar almost to the top, leaving about an inch of space.

2. Completely cover the material with the glycerin and water blend.

   a. For fresh plants, fill the jar with vegetable glycerin only, until all of the plant material is covered.

   b. If you are working with dried plant material, blend a mixture of three parts vegetable glycerin and one part distilled water in a bowl, and pour this into the jar of dried herbs.

3. Store your glycerite in a cool, dark place for four to six weeks to brew; shake your jar daily to help the infusion process along.

4. When it is time to strain the glycerite, use a cheesecloth to do the job. You will likely need to squeeze the cheesecloth to get all the thick glycerin out of the plant material and into the bottle in which you choose to store it.

5. Store your glycerite in a cool dark cabinet or in the refrigerator for an extended shelf life. A Glycerite is shelf stable 12–36 months. You will probably use it earlier than that.

   Dosages will vary depending on the issue and the plant used, but generally one would take five milliliter doses every three to four hours as needed. Glycerites can last anywhere from one to three years in the fridge or up to

two years in a dark cabinet. I recently finished a glycerite with chamomile and Passionflower with this recipe for bedtime and it not only relaxes us when needed, but everyone loves the taste.

Decoctions

A decoction is made with water, but is stronger than a tea. Only roots, barks or seeds are used in a decoction. As a general rule, add one teaspoon to one tablespoon of dried herbal parts per cup of water when making a decoction.

1. Add the herbs and cold water to a pot.

2. Next, bring this to a boil.

3. Place a lid on the pot and simmer gently for twenty to forty minutes. Be sure to turn it down to simmer after bringing to a boil, as continued high heat can destroy some of the herbal benefits you're after.

4. Remove the decoction from heat and let it cool. When it's fully cooled, it is ready for consumption.

   Depending on the need, you can drink anywhere from one to three cups a day. The liquid must be kept in the refrigerator and should ideally be used within forty-eight hours. Decoctions are often used when a tea isn't strong enough to tackle the issue.

Nourishing Herbal Infusions

Nourishing herbal infusions are strong drinks that help heal the body. They are much stronger than tea, and are used at times when a stronger remedy is needed to combat an issue. These beverages are rich in a variety of nutrients and healing plant compounds. They should be created and promptly stored in the refrigerator. Herbal infusions are ideal for those who need daily support from certain herbs.

1. Bring a quart (1 liter) of water to the boil on a stove.

2. While waiting for the water to boil, place one ounce(30 g) of dried herbs in a quart-sized glass jar.

3. Once the water has boiled, dump it carefully into the quart jar and let this steep for four to ten hours. For a stronger infusion, follow these steps before bedtime and let the infusion steep overnight.

4. When done steeping, strain out the water and drink this throughout the day and evening.

Try to consume an infusion within twenty-four hours of its production, leaving it in the refrigerator between uses. A good time to give an herbal infusion is after sickness, when a person needs to promote recovery and build up strength. My great grandmother Alma was well known for her herbal infusions. People from all over the county would come to her for an infusion to help them recover from sickness.

Syrups

Syrups are a fun herbal remedy for children, as they are sweet and pleasant-tasting. They are created following the same protocol as you would a decoction.

1. Create a medicinal infusion or decoction as directed previously.

2. When you have done this, remove it from heat and strain it through a cheesecloth or strainer. Let it cool a little before doing this to avoid burning yourself.

3. Next, measure the amount of liquid you have.

4. Measure out an equal amount of raw honey to the amount of infusion or decoction you have, and blend them together well. Some herbal syrup recipes call for one to two cups of sugar, instead of honey, to make herbal syrup. But sugar is not healthy, especially for children; it weakens the immune system and can be counterproductive to healing. If you have to use sugar, use organic cane sugar, or raw maple syrup, instead of processed granulated sugar.

5. Store in the refrigerator for a longer shelf life of up to 6 months.

Dosage varies depending on the issue at hand, and is also different for children. It often consists of one half teaspoon to one tablespoon, taken one to three times a day. A popular syrup is elderberry syrup, taken as an immunity–boosting tonic. Syrups for coughs are also commonly used; thyme syrup is one that my best friend's family uses frequently, with great success. In the case of cough syrups, the addition of honey, if possible, is important as it is especially good for coughs.

Herbal Lozenges

Herbal lozenges, also referred to as "herbal candy," are another great way to prepare herbs for children. They are also a great choice for adults who find it difficult to take other formulations. They make excellent cough drops, to soothe a sore throat and spasmodic coughing, because they take time to dissolve in the mouth and allow you to suck on them, thereby helping to coat the throat.

1. Add one to two tablespoons of the dried herbs of your choice to two cups of water in a pot on the stove.

2. Bring this to a boil and then allow it to reduce by half.

3. Once the liquid is reduced, strain out the herbs.

4. Add 1.5 cups of raw honey to the liquid and return this to a pan over medium heat.

5. Stir everything together well with a wooden spoon or spatula.

6. Let this boil until it reaches 300°F (150°C). You may need to use a candy thermometer if you are not a seasoned candy maker. (I swear my mom could make candy with her eyes closed and never used a thermometer, but I am not nearly as experienced in this department so I have to make use of the tools available.) You will notice the syrup becoming thicker as you stir it.

7. When the recommended temperature has been reached, take a spoon and drop small amounts of the mixture onto parchment paper. These drops will harden in a few hours to a "lozenge" consistency.

8. To prevent them from sticking together in the jar, sprinkle

them with ground cinnamon (*Cinnamomum verum* or *Cinnamomum cassia*) or ginger (*Zingiber officinale*) when they cool, and toss them around so they are fully coated.

9. Place these in a jar for use as needed.

Herbal Pills and Capsules

Some people are not able to tolerate drinking herbal liquids, so they opt for capsules or pills instead.

1. Capsules:

   a. Grind your herbs into powder form using a mortar and pestle, a quality blender that has the capability of grinding dried plants into flour, or a flour grinder.

   b. Once you have herbal powder, you can add it to capsules using a capsule press or a device that holds your capsules upright so you can place the powder inside.

Capsules are harder for younger children to take, but you can create herbal pills for them to use instead.

2. Pills:

   a. Combine the powdered herb with raw honey and carefully blend these until you create a moldable consistency. The amount of honey and powder will vary depending on the herbs used and how many pills you wish to make. This will also vary depending on a person's age/weight. Research the herb you plan on working with to make sure it is safe and has no contraindications for children, as well as to determine a correct dosage of powder to work with. Whatever amount of herbal powder you use, use only enough honey to reach a moldable consistency.

   b. Roll small amounts of this into a pill shape and place the pills in the refrigerator to cool and harden (Herbal Academy, 2021).

These aren't meant to be swallowed whole, like pharmaceutical pills; rather, they break apart in your mouth. The honey makes them much easier to swallow. Instruct your child to chew them like other chewable pills, before swallowing them. My aunt Marge often makes pills this way for her children and they quite like the taste of them, which makes it much easier to medicate them.

Herbal Baths

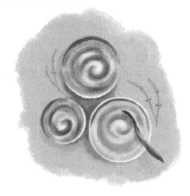

Poultices

Poultices are one of the simplest ways to use herbs, for children and adults alike. These are made by mashing up a fresh herb and applying it to an area. If you're using dried herbs simply mash these up and add a little water to get a thicker consistency for applying them to an area. Some poultices work well in whole-leaf form, such as cabbage leaves and comfrey leaves. These can simply be applied to the area without mashing, and then held in place with plastic wrap or bandages while they dry. Poultices work great to stop bleeding from cuts and scrapes (yarrow is the best herb for this) or to relieve pain from an insect sting (aloe, lavender, or plantain works well in this case).

For children who have trouble falling asleep (or adults too, for that matter), herbal baths can be a powerful remedy to add to the bedtime routine. In addition, they are perfect for soothing the skin of children affected by chicken pox or irritating rashes. Herbal baths don't have to be messy. To prevent clogging your drain, try adding dried or fresh herbs to a muslin bag with a drawstring (the bigger, reusable tea bags work great for this as well).

1. Fill the bag with anywhere from three tablespoons to a half cup of herbs and shut the drawstring tightly to prevent any from escaping into the water.

2. Allow this to sit in the bath water as the tap is running, and then leave it in the water throughout the duration of your child's bath.

Lavender is a useful herb for bedtime. Oatmeal, chickweed, and calendula are useful herbs for skin rashes. My oldest daughter absolutely loves taking a bath with her bath teas, as we call them. Her favorite combination so far is lavender and chamomile, for relaxation before going to sleep.

Poultices of jewelweed make great treatment for rashes and skin irritations because they help to soothe and cool the area. A fun fact that my grandmother taught me about jewelweed is that it often grows near poison ivy plants which, she said, was nature's way of helping us know how to counteract the ivy's itchy effects. Be sure to do the scratch test with herbs that you consider using for a poultice, to check for a topical allergic reaction; some, such as angelica, may cause contact dermatitis. Fresh stinging nettle should be avoided due to the stinging hairs that give it its name. Others known to cause skin irritation are cow parsnip, rue, dog fennel, and primrose.

How to Store your Herbal Formulations

If you want your herbal creations to stay fresh for as long as possible, it is important that you store them in the correct way.

Dried herbs

1. If you have a collection of dried herbs to use for teas, decoctions and other formulations, it is important to understand that these will begin to lose their potency after one year.

2. The best way to store dried herbs is out of direct sunlight and in airtight, glass jars.

3. Many people opt to store their dried herbs in glass jars in a cabinet with doors. Make sure they are stored in an area that is dry, as moisture can cause mold to grow on your herbs.

4. The temperature of your storage area should not fluctuate or you'll risk damaging the potency of your herbs.

5. You can place little dehumidifier bags in your jars of herbs to suck moisture out of the air, and there are even bags available to keep the oxygen levels lower in the container.

6. If, at the end of a year, your dried herbs are still not used up, you can either process them into formulations such as tinctures, glycerites and syrups, or you can

freeze them in envelopes (just make sure to label everything well). They will keep their flavor, color, and properties for up to twelve months in a frozen state. When ready to use, simply take them out, defrost and use as normal.

Using **dried herbs** is a good way to extend the shelf life of your herbal products, but fresh herbs make strong and potent products. Fresh herbs can be used in alcohol–based formulations, like tinctures, with no issues (as long as the entire herb is covered as instructed). But for oil infusions, it is better to use dried herbs because fresh herbs have a higher water content and this can promote the development of mold and result in spoilage. Some herbs have to be used in a fresh or recently–dried form when making an oil infusion. The most notable examples of this are when preparing lemon balm for its antiherpes properties, preparing lobelia and St. John's wort flowers for their antiasthma properties, and preparing jewelweed for a treatment against poison ivy exposure. In these cases one must be very careful to remove all water from the oil, and keep an eye on the product for spoilage.

Herbal formulations with a high water content, such as teas, decoctions, and infusions do not keep for as long and are prone to spoilage and mold. These should always be refrigerated between uses and should be used within forty-eight hours. Look for the presence of a "bloom" of mold in these formulations. It often appears as a ghost–like blob, floating around in the liquid. If you attempt to use a product with a bloom in it, you could become very sick. Always play it safe and throw out products that have what appears to be a bloom of mold. A friend of mine, Alicia, received some bad advice one time, being told that she could simply scoop out the bloom and her infusion would be fine. She followed the advice and wound up sick for three days. She was miserable, but the lesson was remembered from then on.

For **oil-based products like oil infusions and salves**, store these in a cool, dark area with consistent temperatures. Fluctuations in temperatures cause products to spoil more quickly. In addition, if the temperature is allowed to get too hot, salves can easily melt and spill out of their containers. These products are considered to be good until the expiration date on the oils that were used to make them.

Products like **glycerites** will last longer if kept refrigerated. **Syrups** have a higher water content, but the honey helps to preserve them for longer. Just to be safe, however, try to use up an herbal syrup within three months.

The freezer can be handy for storage when it comes to keeping certain herbal formulations fresh and ready to use when needed. For example, if you happen to make a big batch of a decoction, infusion, or tea, you can always:

1. Pour what you do not use into ice cube trays and freeze this overnight.

2. The next day, simply pop the herbal ice cubes out of the tray and place them in a plastic freezer bag.

3. Label the bag with the name of the herbal preparation and when it was created.

4. The ice cube size is perfect for quick and easy melting. Avoid melting your herbal ice cubes in the microwave, as this destroys any medicinal properties they have.

Welcome to Our World, Little Earthling

(The First Moments)

A child's first moments in this world are some of the most overwhelming and important. Newborns don't have highly developed vision, but they can see their parents looking down on them for the first time. This visual bonding experience is vital to early development and their eyes need to be kept unobstructed to allow for this.

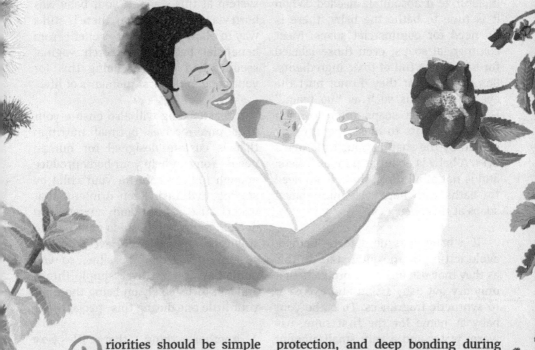

Priorities should be simple at this point. A baby needs to be able to see his or her parent(s) and experience skin-to-skin contact on a parent's chest, if possible. This establishes feelings of safety, protection, and deep bonding during these first moments.

Baby will be covered in a thick, white substance called vernix. While this may make you think the baby is unclean, vernix is an important and purposeful part of the baby's protection system. Vernix helps to protect the baby's delicate skin from being "pickled" while soaking in the amniotic fluid for nine months. It also serves a purpose after birth when it helps protect the baby's delicate skin from drying out. In short, there is no need for a bath at this time unless your baby was covered in blood or other contaminants after birth. Let nature do its job to protect and hydrate your little one's skin.

To help moisturize the baby's skin, gently massage the vernix into it. Baby's skin can dry out, especially around the ankles and feet, so keep this area covered with socks and only moisturize if absolutely needed. When it is time to bathe the baby, there is no need for commercial soaps. Most commercial soaps, even those labeled for babies, are full of toxic ingredients. Some claim that they do not hurt the eyes, with labels such as "no tears." However, these soaps often contain numbing agents to mask the stinging caused by the soap in your little one's eyes. A baby is about as pure as it gets, and is not at all dirty; there is no need for baths with harsh, chemical-laden soaps at this stage.

If a baby does need to be bathed, avoid letting the hospital staff do this as they may use unsavory products that only dry out baby's skin and expose it to synthetic fragrances. To bathe your baby at home for the first time, use warm water and a very small amount of unscented liquid castile soap (only a thimble full or 50 ml) in the tub. Blend the soap in the water and gently wash your baby with a cloth, avoiding the face and eyes. Baby's face should be washed with warm water only.

In addition to delaying a bath, consider delaying umbilical cord clamping as well. Instead of cutting off the stem cell-rich blood, allow the baby to reap the benefits of this amazing process. Not fussing over the umbilical cord and rather allowing it to do what nature intended will also give you more uninterrupted time bonding with your little one.

Babies born vaginally will likely have been exposed to many beneficial bacteria that can help build their microbiome. This is nature's way of beginning the process of strengthening his or her immune system. This, along with breastfeeding, is the best way you can take care of your child's immune system at this stage. If your baby was born via cesarean section, there is still a way to allow your child to benefit from beneficial bacteria. Research vaginal seeding and consider doing this for your baby in the first moments of life.

Breastfeeding will also ensure your little one receives optimal nutrition that is custom designed for human needs. You can help your body produce enough milk to care for your child by staying hydrated. Keep drinking that water! Also, stress and anxiety can deplete milk supply, so do your best to stay calm and positive. Have a support system in place, if possible, so you don't have to fret over simple things and can focus solely on being there for your little one during this special time.

Another thing that is very important, especially in the early days when the baby is still learning to latch on and suck, is nipple stimulation. Mother's milk supply is determined by the stimulation the nipples received twelve hours before. You should allow

the baby to remain latched for a time even if the baby falls asleep. If you can't get the baby to cooperate, your partner can provide the necessary stimulation.

Supplemental feeding by bottle limits stimulation even more. It is very important to encourage nursing for as long as the baby can, preferably until the breast is dry, and to switch breasts at least every other feeding. If the baby won't do this, or is too weak to feed until the breast is empty, pump by hand or use a purchased gadget. Mom may think she can't produce enough milk when often all she needs is more stimulation. Once stronger, the baby will provide this.

Breastfeeding and breast milk are much more complex and sophisticated than most people realize. Human milk not only boosts a baby's immune system to help fight off viruses and bacteria, it can also help fight off parasitic infections. According to the Health Foundations Birth Center, breastfeeding also reduces a baby's risk of many different diseases later in life. Some of these diseases include diabetes, leukemia, autoimmune disease, and obesity. In addition, breastfed infants have a lower risk of sudden infant death syndrome (SIDS).

A mother can actually heal faster postpartum when she breastfeeds. Breastfeeding your newborn helps your uterus return more rapidly to pre-pregnancy size, and may even reduce postpartum blood loss. Mom benefits from breastfeeding in even more ways as it reduces a mother's risk of ovarian and breast cancer, osteoporosis, and heart disease. In fact, the longer a mother can breastfeed, the more she reduces her risk of developing these diseases.

Breastfeeding also helps a mom return to pre-pregnancy weight faster because it burns over 1000 calories a day just to produce breast milk.

Breast milk actually changes its nutritional profile as your baby grows. In the first moments of your baby's life, it contains an especially nutrient-rich substance called colostrum. Make sure your focus, when the baby arrives, is on allowing him or her to breastfeed as much as possible and get plenty of this nutritious and immune-boosting substance. The nutritional profile of breast milk can actually change in a day, if needed. This helps adjust for sickness (more hydrating and immune-boosting milk is produced) or even temperature (hot weather produces more hydrating breastmilk).

Aside from all the health benefits breastfeeding holds for both mom and baby, it also helps them bond more closely. Breast milk contains compounds that help babies calm down and fall asleep more quickly, which means that breastfed babies sleep more, on average, than formula-fed babies. This benefits both mom and baby by helping mom get the rest she needs as well.

It is vital to keep the surrounding environment quiet and calm during your baby's first moments of life. This is because your baby is learning what to do. It may not be outwardly apparent, but your baby actually has to learn quite a bit in the first moments of life – how to breathe, how to get milk into the mouth, and how to swallow. Too many noises and smells can make it harder for a baby to do these things. There is no need for hustle and bustle in your baby's first moments. It is not necessary to measure the baby, take weight, or do footprints until the baby has had time to learn these skills. Focus on skin-to-skin contact, breastfeeding, and bonding for at least the first hour of life.

Of course, for a number of reasons, breastfeeding is sometimes not possible. In these instances, simply put, fed is best. Skin-to-skin contact, while bottle feeding, can still help create the bond that baby (and you) need during those first few days of life. Your baby needs you more than anything. One way to get the same health benefits of breastmilk without actually breastfeeding is through a milk donor, which is most often someone who has an abundance of milk and wishes to share it with others. You can find such a donor in a variety of ways, including through your doctor or local lactation consultant.

One issue that may come up is a condition called jaundice. This is caused because the baby's liver isn't mature enough to get rid of bilirubin (a normal part of the pigment released from the breakdown of used red blood cells) in the bloodstream, although it can be a sign of an underlying problem as well.

It is more common in preterm babies and breastfed babies. It presents with yellowing of the skin and whites of the eyes, and can be diagnosed by a physical exam and a blood test. Hospitals will check for signs of jaundice before they discharge you and your baby.

One of my middle children had a very mild case of jaundice which wasn't actually discovered until our very first doctor's appointment following her birth. Because it usually appears between the second and fourth day after birth that first appointment with your doctor is important. We had to go back to the hospital for a couple of days and the staff laid her in a special baby bed equipped with a light for phototherapy. This common form of treatment changes the shape and structure of bilirubin molecules in such a way that they can be excreted in both the urine and stool. In more severe cases, intravenous transfusion of an immunoglobulin (a blood protein that can reduce levels of antibodies) or an exchange transfusion will be performed. These cases are far more uncommon and only used when absolutely needed.

Feel Comfortable Yet?

(The First Five Days)

While the first moments of a baby's life are often filled with peace and joy, the moments that follow can be quite confusing for first-time parents, or even seasoned parents! The first five days are some of the most hectic because you are getting to know your new little one and he or she is getting to know you. But you are not the only new feature of baby's world; the surroundings are also brand new, and so much bigger than what baby has been used to. After all, your precious bundle of joy has been suspended in warm amniotic fluid inside your womb for the past nine months. This was a tight place of darkness and comfort, whereas now there is light and space and the new sensation of being able to extend arms and legs, and feel the cool air on the skin. At this point, a baby has to adapt to a completely new living environment.

Babies are working out these new kinks during the first five days of life. They will slowly begin to familiarize themselves with their new living space and all the new faces. During this time, avoid taking them to new places and allow them to get to know what matters most to them: their family and their new home. This is a time to stay home with your baby and cater to his or her needs, which may be few or many depending on the baby. Most babies sleep a lot during this time, as they did in the womb. While still inside, however, they were used to constant movement, as they were living inside a human being. This is why many babies like a rocking motion to get to sleep or calm down.

At this stage, all baths after the very first one (described previously) need only be done with warm water. Avoid bathing your baby every day, as this dries out the skin fast. Weekly baths are more than sufficient. Your baby will need some moisturizing after a bath. Instead of reaching for a commercial baby lotion, which may contain synthetic fragrances (linked to hormone disruption and allergies) and alcohol (placed in lotions to make them appear to evaporate quickly, but which dries out skin), you can moisturize with a simple carrier oil, such as coconut oil or raw shea butter. These oils are solid at room temperature, but melt easily when placed on your hand. Massage this into the baby's skin, but don't put it on too thickly, as the skin is more delicate and porous than adult skin. To keep the moisture in, clothe your baby well by covering all the moisturized areas. You can also massage coconut oil or shea butter into the baby's scalp. Many babies have issues with dried-out skin on the scalp in the first months of life. Place a thin hat over the area after application.

At this point in your child's life, there is no need to begin introducing herbs or any other products because a baby has very sensitive and permeable skin. This means it soaks up the things it is exposed to more readily than adult skin. This puts babies at a much higher risk of allergic reactions. They are also more prone to water loss as a result of their skin permeability. Simply put, your baby's skin is fragile and needs to be moisturized with simple ingredients rather than with a blend of many ingredients that could cause an allergic reaction or dermatitis. Many pediatricians recommend introducing one food at a time when your baby begins eating solids; this is done to help pinpoint any potential allergens more easily. The same goes for herbs and other products that you expose your baby to. Keep it simple so that you are better able to pinpoint the causes of any allergies.

During these first five days, your baby also has to learn how to breastfeed, if this is the route you and your baby have taken. This can be tricky for some babies, although much of it comes naturally. If you notice your baby having significant trouble with latching on, it may be time to ask your pediatrician to check for tongue or lip ties. A lactation consultant is a wonderful resource for answering any questions regarding breastfeeding. An unborn baby is used to getting the nutrition he or she needs through the umbilical cord, already digested by the mother, but after birth the baby's stomach must begin to digest breast milk on its own. While breast milk is perfectly designed for human infants, issues can still occur. Most often, these issues arise because of foods the mother is eating, such as garlic, spicy foods, or dairy products. If you notice your baby spitting up frequently or fussing after feedings, start adjusting your diet to eliminate potential allergens.

Another common trigger is acidic foods, such as citrus and tomatoes.

These items may increase the acidity of breast milk and cause reflux or gastrointestinal discomfort for the baby. When I began to nurse my first baby, I noticed that every time I ate broccoli, my baby would get very gassy. After researching and talking to my mother, I realized that broccoli can cause gassiness in adults so it stood to reason that it may also cause problems for a nursing baby. Much to my sadness, because I love broccoli, I stopped eating it for a while until my baby's digestive system was more mature. I was able to resume after a few months, and today she loves broccoli as much as I do. Issues can also arise with formula, and you should see your pediatrician for a potential change in brand, if your baby seems intolerant to the one you use.

Do Those Shining Eyes Recognize Me?

(The First Month)

During the first month, your baby is starting to get settled into life on the other side of the womb. There are several milestones to look for during this time, including the ability to focus on objects, kick legs and develop those muscles, and cry to communicate needs. During this stage, keep in mind that less is more when it comes to the products you expose your baby to. In this chapter, you will learn what to expect in the first month, and I will describe some extra gentle remedies for treating various issues your baby may face.

During this time, it is important to focus on being a strong presence in your baby's life and begin to understand what is needed when your baby cries. Crying isn't always a sign that your baby is hungry, although hunger is a common issue because babies grow in leaps and bounds during the first few months. A baby cannot speak or communicate, so the only way that he or she is able to get what is needed is through crying. This can be quite frustrating for a parent, especially

a new parent. It may feel as though your baby isn't happy and is constantly fussy. However, keep in mind that crying is an important milestone at this stage. You will eventually learn to distinguish different types of cries, such as hunger cries, tired cries, bored cries, and cries indicating the need for a diaper change. For me personally, this was a hard lesson to learn. As a first-time mom, I often felt helpless when my baby cried. Eventually, though, I learned. And so will you.

Other milestones to watch for at this time include reflexes like the palmar reflex (this is when baby grabs your finger) and the moro reflex (this is when baby jumps in reaction to being startled). Senses like vision are still developing, and your baby can see you clearly if you stay within eight to twelve inches (20–30 cm) from his or her face. Don't be worried if your baby's eyes sometimes cross at this stage – the muscles that control eye movement are still developing as well. It is always unnerving, yet somewhat hilarious, to see the random ways in which their eyes move. Hearing is still developing too, but your baby's hearing is good enough to be able to recognize the voices of mom and dad (that actually starts in the womb!). The sense of smell is also quite well developed, and your baby can actually recognize your scent. As far as taste goes, your baby can distinguish bitter from sweet, but of course prefers the sweetness of milk. Baby can also taste when mom has eaten certain foods, by how her milk tastes. Of all the senses, your baby's sense of touch is the most highly developed during this time, so make sure to give plenty of snuggles!

According to the National Sleep Foundation, your baby needs anywhere from fourteen to seventeen hours of sleep a day. This may sound like a lot, but it may not feel that way when a baby wakes regularly to eat. Create a safe environment for your baby to get this much-needed rest. This includes a comfortable place to sleep, without pillows, crib bumpers, stuffed animals, blankets, or objects that could inhibit free breathing. Consider purchasing a sleep sack for your baby to wear instead of using blankets in the crib. Some parents find noise machines useful to simulate the comforting noises your baby may have heard in utero.

Lavender Tea Remedy for Mom

At this point in your baby's development, it is not recommended to use herbs to help him or her sleep. However, as a parent, you may find an herbal tea helpful to take care of yourself! If you have trouble winding down after a feeding, or are dealing with stress and anxiety, consider drinking a cup of lavender tea. Lavender is safe to drink when you are breastfeeding. It helps to provide calm and allow you to destress. Infuse one teaspoon of lavender buds in a cup of hot water for ten minutes and enjoy.

During the first month, many parents of newborns have to deal with colic. Colic is frequent, prolonged crying and fussiness in an otherwise healthy infant. Don't be too quick to diagnose your baby with colic though, as there is more to it than just fussiness in an infant. A truly colicky baby exhibits other symptoms apart from the crying. Look for tightly closed or widely opened knees, balled fists, gas, flailing limbs, and small bouts of holding breath.

If you ask your pediatrician, he or she might tell you to look for the rule of threes with colic. That is, at least three hours of crying, at least three days a week, for at least three weeks. If you indeed have a colicky baby, there are some strategies you can use to try and lessen the discomfort. Try these before resorting to an herbal remedy for colic: change your diet if you are breastfeeding, or change formula if you are formula feeding. Do not change the formula without first consulting a professional. Opt for something organic and lactose free, if you do make a change. Breastfeeding moms should consider cutting out dairy products, spicy foods, acidic foods, garlicky foods, soy, corn, peanuts, wheat, caffeine, and gassy foods like broccoli, Brussels sprouts, cabbage, cauliflower, onions, and green peppers. Try cutting out one food at a time so you know which one(s) in particular may trigger your baby's discomfort.

In addition to dietary change, try swaddling your baby. There are several products you can buy to make swaddling easier. Swaddling helps wrap your baby up to mimic the conditions of the womb. It can calm and settle babies, making it easier for them to get to sleep and have a decent stretch of sleep. Finally, try

offering a pacifier. The sucking reflex calms many babies and can help them focus on a different sensation. Some parents also have success using a white noise machine, and still others find that crying lessens when the baby is held for an extended amount of time. Colic usually starts around the first two to three weeks of a baby's life and peaks in severity by week six. After the first few months, colic tends to disappear. If you are struggling during this time, ask for help from your partner or a friend for a while so you can get some rest or take some time for yourself.

If your baby meets all the criteria for colic and is inconsolable after trying all of the above methods, you can create an herbal remedy to help soothe the stomach and ease gas. Perform a "scratch" test before introducing *any* herbs to your baby. You can do this by making a tea with an herb (do one herb at a time) and applying a small amount to your baby's inner arm. Wait twenty-four hours to see if there is any negative reaction.

Colic Remedy: Fennel and Spearmint Tea for Baby and Mom

This colic remedy involves making a simple tea with fennel (*Foeniculum vulgare*) seeds and spearmint (*Mentha spicata*) leaves. Fennel is known for its antispasmodic effects on the gastrointestinal system. It can help ease pain from gas and bloating. Spearmint is more child-friendly than peppermint and safer for use in children. It helps calm an upset stomach. Add a half teaspoon of fennel seeds and a half teaspoon of spearmint leaves to a tea bag and infuse them in a cup of sterile hot water for five to ten minutes.

Use a dropper to give your baby five to ten drops of this, to start with. If baby seems to do well with this tea after a few hours, you can give five to ten more drops as needed. The tea should be refrigerated between uses. All water-based herbal formulations should be thrown out after twenty-four hours. You will have a lot of this tea left over since you are only administering five to ten drops at a time. Don't let it go to waste! Mom can drink this tea and pass its benefits through her breast milk as well. Just make sure to drink the remainder within twenty-four hours.

Gentle Remedy for Cradle Cap

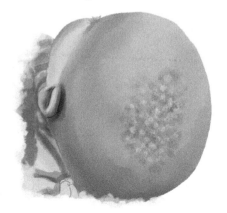

Apart from colic and fussiness, another issue that seems to plague babies at this time is cradle cap and overall dry skin. Keep things simple for your baby's first month of life, when treating skin issues. Remember, a baby's skin is much more porous and sensitive than adult skin! For moderate cradle cap and dry skin, start by massaging organic coconut oil into the scalp and any dry areas. Coconut oil is gentle and most skin types can tolerate it well. Leave the coconut oil on for fifteen minutes before gently washing the hair with warm water. Afterwards, use a fine-tooth comb to comb out any flakes that are stuck in the hair. Avoid doing this more than once daily, or the scalp could dry out due to the daily washing (not the coconut oil treatment). The root cause of cradle cap is not known, but some researchers believe it might be caused by a fungal issue or overactive sebaceous glands. If this is the case, coconut oil is the perfect remedy because it is naturally antifungal and might even help reduce sebum when used over a period of time. A friend of mine, Tiffany, had her baby a couple years ago. She tried several different things to treat her baby's cradle cap, but to no avail – until she finally tried coconut oil. It worked like a charm.

Remedy for Rashes Caused by Diaper, Drool, and Dryness

Many parents know the frustrating fight of keeping diaper rash at bay. It is bound to happen when your baby's sensitive skin is covered with a diaper and exposed regularly to wet conditions. First and foremost, change your baby's diaper as often as possible, especially before and sometimes after each feeding. Do what you can to ensure your baby doesn't sit in a wet diaper for too long. A good offense goes a long way in preventing diaper rash as well! One of the most effective herbs for treating diaper rash (and just about any other rash) is pot marigold (*Calendula officinalis*). The flower of this plant has been used as an herbal remedy for skin irritation for centuries. It is very soothing to irritated, red, and inflamed skin.

You can make your own diaper rash cream by following the salve protocol for beginners, using coconut oil. After infusing the pot marigold in coconut oil, allow this to cool and it will return to a salve-like consistency. Keep this handy, near your changing table, because it definitely doesn't hurt to apply it with each diaper change. If you can have this on hand, you may never experience a diaper rash at all because you will be able to "nip it in the bud." Be sure to dry the baby's bottom with a tissue after using wet wipes, but before applying salve. This aids in eliminating wetness.

Calendula (also known as pot marigold) salve is another wonderful remedy for skin irritation caused by drooling (which happens later when your baby's teeth begin to emerge). Simply apply it under the chin (get in between all of those skin folds) or anywhere else that drool causes issues. Make sure the area is clean and dry before applying the salve. And that isn't where this salve's usefulness ends, either! It can be your go-to salve for any kind of skin irritation, such as rashes, red and inflamed areas, and even dry lips. Any time your baby's skin needs a little help, this is the salve to reach for.

The Surprisingly Effective Remedy for Baby Acne

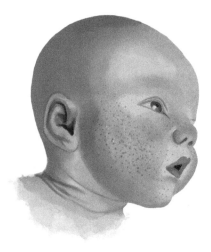

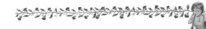

Some parents look forward to taking photos of their newborn, and wait a few weeks for the opportunity (because after all, it can be kind of hectic to accomplish this in the first week). Some are horrified to see that, just before they are ready to have photos taken, their perfect baby suddenly has a face full of little pimples! When your baby is around two weeks old, there is a chance baby acne could emerge. There is no reason to panic. Baby acne, or neonatal cephalic pustulosis, is a very common condition. In fact, around three in ten infants will experience this. It is characterized by little bumps or pustules on the baby's forehead, chin, and cheeks. It may even occur on the eyelids. It is not harmful to your baby and doesn't pose a health threat. This condition often goes away on its own, within a few weeks. However, it can be quite frustrating as a parent to see your precious little one with a face full of pustules! There are some things you can do at home to help take care of this.

First, keep your baby's face as clean as possible at all times. No abrasive soaps are needed for this. Simply wipe it with a warm, damp cloth several times a day. In addition to keeping your baby's face clean, you can treat it with a naturally antimicrobial substance that you will find right in your own home. This substance is your own breast milk! That's right. Breastmilk contains a compound called lauric acid which is naturally antibacterial and can target the bacteria that cause acne. Put a little on a cotton ball and, after wiping your baby's face with a warm washcloth, dab the cotton ball on affected areas. Since breastmilk is all natural and perfectly made for human infants, you can be sure it is completely safe for your baby, even when applied topically.

Some moms even swear by breast milk for treating pinkeye bacteria! They claim that dropping breast milk into the affected eye clears it right up. The verdict on whether that is a truly effective remedy is still not in.

Oatmeal is another treatment for both baby acne and skin rashes. It is incredibly soothing to the skin and also helps reduce inflammation. This may be one reason why it helps clear up baby acne so well. You can make a simple paste with organic oatmeal by grinding up a small amount in a mortar and pestle and then adding a very small amount of water until the mixture has a paste-like consistency. Apply this to affected areas for ten minutes and then rinse it off. Do not get this anywhere near your baby's eyes, but rather focus on the chin and lower portion of the cheeks. Repeat this once daily and feel free to use breast milk between treatments, if necessary.

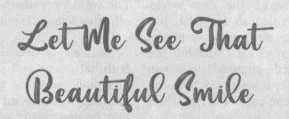

Let Me See That Beautiful Smile

(Two to Four Months)

This period is a time of adorable milestones! Babies smile more and even laugh or giggle at your funny antics. They are not only responding to new voices, they are also responding to changes in the tone of your voice. Babies can now tell when you are angry or happy. Babbling begins in this phase as well. They may also start making more speech-like sounds in an attempt to communicate. In addition, they are beginning to recognize and respond to their name. If you say your baby's name, he or she may well turn and look at you. This is a time to focus on keeping that milk supply going, encouraging safe and restful sleep, and keeping your baby safe from falls.

On a physical level, your baby is now growing by leaps and bounds. Since their neck muscles are more developed, they are better able to hold up their heads. And when their feet are placed on a hard surface, they may try to push down with their legs. A big accomplishment at this time is the ability to roll over from the front to the back. Once babies learn how to do this, they are much more mobile, so avoid sitting them on a bed with no railing. Giving your baby plenty of tummy time at this stage is important so they can work their arm and neck muscles. They should be able to lift themselves up on their elbows when lying tummy down. When playing and interacting with your baby, you may find that he is beginning to love toys. Between the ages of two and four months, a baby can hold a toy and shake it to play, as well as being able to take a swing at a toy that dangles overhead.

With all that is going on in your baby's physical and mental growth, there are also some issues that may arise during this time. If you choose to immunize your baby, know that this may cause a fever to develop. While some doctors recommend acetaminophen, this depletes the glutathione your baby needs for a strong immune system and also makes the blood-brain barrier more permeable. Rather than using acetaminophen, try a tepid bath or a cool compress instead. Monitor the fever and take your baby to the hospital if the fever gets over 101°F (38°C) because, while a fever is the body's natural way of dealing with infections, a high fever in infants can be dangerous. Watch for screaming, extreme fussiness, rashes, and other signs of swelling or a reaction.

Decrease in Milk Supply

Another issue that many women face at this point is a decrease in milk supply. Most mothers have a milk supply that peaks at around six weeks and then may start to plateau or decrease. There are many reasons for this, but some important ones include vitamin deficiency, stress, and certain foods and herbs that affect supply. If you are concerned that you don't have enough milk to keep your baby healthy, the first thing you should do is see a lactation consultant. This will help you determine the steps you can take to keep milk supply up. In addition, make sure to keep feeding your baby on demand. This stimulates milk supply. You can also pump to simulate demand, which should help increase your supply. Your lactation consultant can help you if you have issues pumping. Be sure to stay adequately hydrated and eat properly. Oatmeal is known for increasing milk supply and is very healthy for you and baby. While having a baby can be stressful and a lot of work, do what you can to avoid being stressed. Stress and anxiety are major setbacks to developing and maintaining milk supply.

Below, you will find a recipe that my mom passed to me during my first pregnancy. This is a recipe she used, while pregnant with me, to help relieve stress and I also used in my pregnancies.

Nourishing Nettle and Lavender Tea

Stinging nettle may have a fierce name, but this herb is a wonderful source of nourishing vitamins and minerals that can help give a breastfeeding mom the nutrients she needs to support her baby. Lavender is known for its calming and soothing properties. Together, these two herbs combine to create a tea that lowers stress, but provides nutrients for a mother in need of supply help. To create this tea, simply add one teaspoon of lavender buds and one teaspoon of dried and chopped stinging nettle leaves. Infuse these in a cup of hot water for ten to fifteen minutes before drinking. Enjoy one or two cups daily for best results.

Fenugreek (Trigonella foenum-graecum) Tea for Milk Increase

Fenugreek is one of the most popular herbs that mothers around the world turn to for increasing milk supply. If you are having issues with supply, this may help do the trick to get your supply where it needs to be (although some find it has the opposite effect for them). Fenugreek is a seed with a pleasant, maple syrup aroma. It tastes nice in tea and can be used in various recipes for increasing supply. Start by drinking fenugreek in tea and see if this works for you. Infuse two teaspoons of fenugreek seeds in a cup of hot water for fifteen minutes and enjoy this daily. If you still aren't seeing an improvement in supply, increase this to twice daily and try the cookie recipe below. If you see a decrease in supply, stop using fenugreek altogether.

No-Bake Lactation Cookies

What new mom has time to bake? You don't have to bake cookies if you use this recipe! It combines ingredients that help to increase milk supply, and uses protein-rich almond butter. Follow the recipe below to make them:

Ingredients:

- One cup of almond butter
- 1/3 cup of almond flour or oatmeal
- 1/3 cup of brewer's yeast
- Two TBSP of raw honey
- One TBSP ground fenugreek seeds
- One teaspoon of vanilla extract
- Pinch of sea salt
- 1/3 cup of cacao chocolate chips.

Mix all the ingredients well in a bowl. Roll these into small balls and place them in the refrigerator to set. Eat three to four cookies daily.

The Sleep Issue

At two to four months of age, you may notice your baby is sleeping for longer stretches. While this is the case for some parents, others find that their baby is still waking up frequently at night for feeds. Understand that this is still completely normal. Although normal infant behavior, it can be very frustrating for a parent to lose sleep at night on a regular basis. Some babies sleep for longer at this stage, but find it extremely hard to get to sleep initially. They just cannot seem to wind down and find peace. For this issue, you may have success with a calming lavender bath before bedtime:

Calming Lavender Bath

Although it is much safer to use an herb than an essential oil for an infant, lavender oil is considered one of the safest for people of all ages. Make sure to use lavender buds to avoid skin reactions with your precious little one. Fill your baby's bath with warm water and then add a muslin cloth bag, with two tablespoons of lavender buds inside, to the bath. Make sure the drawstring is pulled tight so the buds do not spill out. Allow this to soak in the water with your baby as you bathe her. Sit in the tub with your little one and shut the curtain to trap in the aromatic fumes. Inhalation of lavender can help soothe and calm. A bonus is that lavender is wonderfully nourishing to the skin and can help soothe red and irritated areas.

When it comes to sleep, a lavender bath before bed can provide the calm state your baby needs to get to sleep more easily. A bedtime routine is also a must to ensure your baby gets to sleep each night with ease. A few hours before bedtime, turn off all screens and avoid exposing your baby to them. Blue light from screens is a big culprit for causing insomnia in adults and children alike. Turn down the lights as well, and eliminate all loud and bothersome noises from your home. Maintain an environment of calm and tranquility. Read a book or two and take a lavender bath. Moisturize your baby well with a hydrating moisturizer like the lavender moisturizer recipe below, to help your baby get to sleep more quickly.

Post-Bath Lavender Moisturizer

If a lavender bath is great for getting your baby to sleep, the addition of lavender-infused coconut oil afterwards can create an even more calming atmosphere that is sure to help your baby drift off with a smile. Follow the coconut oil salve-making protocol in Harnessing the Essence of Herbs chapter and use lavender buds as the plant material. Massage this into your baby's skin after each bedtime bath. The lavender in this salve will help soothe skin and the coconut oil is a safe and gentle base for this effective moisturizer. Your baby will fall asleep with the peaceful scent

of lavender lingering in the air.

Acid Reflux

Acid reflux and gastroesophageal reflux disease (GERD) are becoming more common among infants. These conditions cause a baby to spit up more than usual due to the regurgitation of the stomach contents coming back up through the esophagus and into the throat or mouth. Symptoms of this issue include extreme fussiness after eating, and chronic spitting up.

Fennel and Ginger Oil for Acid Reflux

It can be so frustrating to see little ones spitting up, suffering from stomach pain, and refusing to eat. Instead of treating this with potentially harmful pharmaceutical drugs, you can help calm your child's stomach and lower the inflammation that causes reflux with a combination of fennel (*Foeniculum vulgare*), ginger , and coconut oil. Coconut oil is a great base for this remedy because it treats acid issues on its own. It is highly anti-inflammatory and works to calm the stomach to prevent acid reflux. Fennel is good for reflux too, because it contains an enzyme, anethole, that works to regulate gastrointestinal spasms. Ginger also prevents acid reflux, calms the stomach, and encourages healthy digestion. To make this preparation you will need:

- Two teaspoons of each herb (fennel seeds and chopped, dried ginger)
- One cup of coconut oil

Instructions:

1. Set the coconut oil and herb blend in a jar placed in a pan of hot water on low heat. A crockpot with water in it can also be used for this, as long as it is kept on low heat.

2. Allow this to infuse with the lid off for eight to twelve hours, refilling water in the pan or crockpot to maintain a good level.

3. Remove from heat.

4. Strain the oil through a cheesecloth into a clean jar and store in a cool, dark cabinet.

5. Give your child five milliliters of this daily, for best results.

Safety

With your baby reaching more developmental milestones, he may be at a higher risk of falling or getting hurt. A saying that many parents can take to heart at this stage is, "A baby cannot fall off the floor." This may sound like common sense, but many parents make the mistake of underestimating their baby and sitting him up on a counter, bed, couch, or other elevated structure. They assume that the baby is not very mobile yet, so he can't jump off. Unfortunately, babies are more mobile and stronger than most parents realize, and they can find ways to fall off of these surfaces. As previously stated, babies are learning to roll from front to back at this stage, so it is not out of the realm of possibility for the baby to roll off of a surface and onto the floor. If you are putting your baby in a swing or seat, make doubly sure he is buckled in at all times. Don't make the mistake of assuming he can't get out of the device.

When putting your child to sleep, a crib with a lowered mattress is best. If he rolls, there is no chance he can fall off the crib. In a bed, a baby can easily roll off onto the floor if he is not watched closely. If you wish to co-sleep, consider purchasing a crib that fits on the edge of a bed so that your baby is nearby, but has his own space where he cannot fall off or suffocate. Now is still not a good time to cover your baby in blankets or place crib bumpers on the crib. Avoid using pillows or any other objects in the crib.

If your baby experiences a fall, try to stay calm. Easier said than done, I know but baby's emotions feed off yours so if you are calm, baby will calm faster. If your baby doesn't appear to be injured, pick him up and comfort him. Allow him to calm down before assessing his

body for an injury. Once calm, review the situation. What did he fall on? If it is a hard floor, this could be problematic. It is advised that you call the doctor for any fall involving a child who is less than a year old. If your baby appears limp or falls asleep, is bleeding, unconscious, vomiting, or has a seizure, this is a medical emergency that needs to be treated right away. Call an ambulance, but do not move the baby unless he is at immediate risk of further injury. If he is vomiting or having a seizure, you can turn him on his side and keep his neck straight. For bleeding, apply pressure with a cloth until help arrives.

If your baby has fallen, but doesn't appear injured, you are not necessarily out of the woods yet. Monitor your baby closely for the following symptoms: inconsolable crying, a bulging where the soft spot is on the top of their head, excessive sleepiness, fluid or blood coming from ears or nose, vomiting, pupils that aren't the same size, and sensitivity to light or noises. If you notice any of these in your child, seek medical attention right away.

Remember that these things can be avoided by following proper safety protocols mentioned earlier, such as avoiding placing your baby on tall surfaces, using a crib with a tall railing, and buckling him into changing tables, swings, and other potentially harmful devices.

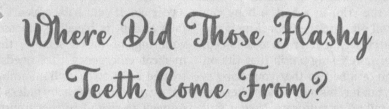

Where Did Those Flashy Teeth Come From?

(Four to Six Months)

Big changes are coming! During this time, your baby will go from being able to roll from front to back (and vice versa) to being able to sit up unassisted, at the age of around six months. This is exciting for babies (and extra scary for parents), because it gives them more independence and a better ability to experience the big world around them. Other changes to expect during this time include reaching for nearby toys, reaching to grab feet when lying on the back, and transferring toys from one hand to the other. These are all signs that your baby's fine motor skills are moving right along!

Your baby's first teeth may also start to appear at this time. This is a stage that many parents complain about because teething babies can be fussy babies. Don't fret because there are plenty of herbal remedies to take care of those teeth! In this chapter,

you will learn how best to care for your baby when it comes to teething, dental care, sleeping, and nutrition, while also nurturing continued muscle and motor development.

If you begin to notice your happy baby suddenly becoming more whiny and temperamental during this time, this could be due to teething. You may also notice a lot more drooling. When baby teeth begin to poke through, you can usually see or feel a raised spot on the gums. Twenty teeth will emerge in all, with ten on the top and ten on the bottom. They won't all come at once, but will gradually fill in your baby's mouth up to age three. The first teeth to come in are often the front lower teeth, followed by the upper middle teeth, molars, and canines. While teething doesn't affect some babies, it is completely normal for it to cause issues like fussiness and drooling in other babies. My last baby was so different from my others. Her teeth came in sooner than my other children's and many times more than one at a time! But, she also didn't seem affected by it near as bad as my other kids were. Oftentimes, I wouldn't know she had another tooth coming in until she bit me!

Rashes and Calendula Salve

Excessive drooling can cause major rashes on your baby's skin due to the constant wet conditions. You can prevent this by applying calendula salve (recipe in previous chapter) to areas under the neck and chin. Apply a liberal amount to your baby after cleaning the area with a warm, wet cloth and drying the area. Do this once or twice daily. Place a bib on your baby as much as possible and be prepared to change it out several times a day. Leaving a wet bib on your baby is just as bad as letting her drool all over her clothes and can make a rash even worse.

If you suspect teething is keeping your child awake at night or causing excessive fussiness, there are some teething remedies you can use to keep your baby comfortable and happy. For daytime, try making teething "popsicles" by following the recipes below:

Breastmilk Teething Popsicle

The simplest and safest teething remedy involves nothing but frozen breastmilk. The only thing you need to purchase is a device to place your frozen breast milk in. There are devices you can buy that allow you to place frozen objects inside an area with mesh netting so your baby can chew but not choke on anything. These devices often have easy-to-grip handles so your baby can hold them and chew with ease. The cold breast milk helps to numb the painful areas of the mouth while also giving your baby a hard surface on which to chew and gnaw. Pump a few ounces of breast milk and then pour it into ice cube trays. Freeze these overnight and then pop them out and place them in a plastic bag for storage in the freezer.

Label your bag so you can keep track of when you made the popsicles. Place one cube in the teething device and sit your baby in an upright position to enjoy. She will definitely need a bib for this, because it can become messy as it melts.

Freezer Washcloth

It has been stated, on several occasions, that less is more when it comes to the remedies you choose to give your baby. Always start with the least invasive remedy and if that doesn't work move on to something else. If the least invasive remedy works, this is great and means you don't have to give your child anything unnecessary to help her feel better. A frozen washcloth is a great trick to try first, with your teething baby. You may be surprised at the relief it brings! The coldness helps to numb teething pain, while the cloth itself makes a nice toy to chew on for further pain relief. Simply rinse a clean washcloth in water and then place it in a plastic bag overnight to freeze. Take it out the next day and let your baby have fun. She will get very wet while playing with this, so have a change of clothes and bib ready.

Chamomile Teething Popsicle

Although a breastmilk teething popsicle is one of the safest ways to numb the pain and satisfy your baby's need to chew, you can also create an herbal popsicle if you find you need a remedy with more potency. Chamomile is one of the most popular herbs for a teething baby because it is safer than some other herbs used for teething and is more readily available. German chamomile (*Matricaria recutita*) and Roman Chamomile (*Anthemis nobilis*) are the most commonly used species. Make sure chamomile is safe for your baby by first performing a scratch test. While it is often safe for the majority of people, it can cause a reaction in some. Create a tea with chamomile by infusing one teaspoon of chamomile in one cup of hot water for ten to fifteen minutes and then pour this into ice cube molds to freeze overnight. Place a cube in the teething device and monitor your baby as she sucks and chews. Try this at bedtime to ensure a restful night's sleep, as chamomile doubles as a sleep-aid in addition to being a soothing pain remedy.

Herbal Teething Compress

An herbal teething compress works much like the frozen washcloth; with this remedy, however, the washcloth is soaked in a soothing herbal tea that can help alleviate teething pain, soothe discomfort, and promote feelings of calm and peace. To make this herbal tea, bring to a boil two teaspoons each of chopped and dried lemon balm and chamomile flowers in one half quart (480 milliliters) of water. Turn off the heat once the blend is boiling, and cover the herbs for ten to twenty minutes. Strain this into a bowl and when it has cooled, soak a clean washcloth in the liquid until it is saturated. Wring it out so it isn't completely soaked and place it in a bag to put in the freezer overnight. Give this to your baby when she is being especially fussy during teething.

Herbal Teething Powder

Chamomile can help calm the body and mind, as well as ease pain. Lemon balm is another gentle herb that can provide soothing relief from anxiety and pain. Together, these make a great remedy to treat teething pain and fussiness. To create this, simply add one teaspoon of chamomile flowers and one teaspoon of dried and chopped lemon balm leaves in a mortar and pestle. Grind these to a powder. Mix everything together well and store in a sterile glass jar. Keep your jar in a cool, dark place to use the herbal mixture as needed. To use, simply take a small pinch and massage it on the affected gum (make sure your hands are clean).

Baltic Amber

Baltic amber necklaces aren't just beautiful. Baltic amber was formed millions of years ago when the sap from Baltic pines fossilized. Pine sap is medicinal and has been used for centuries to treat a wide range of ailments, but many people are not aware that fossilized pine sap, such as Baltic amber, also contains medicinal compounds that work to reduce pain and inflammation. The compound responsible for giving the fossilized sap its medicinal properties is called succinic acid. When your baby

wears these against her skin, they release trace amounts of this healing compound into her body, which then works to soothe the inflammation and pain associated with teething. Since only trace amounts are released, there is no need to worry about reactions or adverse events. Just make sure to take the necklace off when your baby goes to sleep. Monitor your baby at all times to make sure she is safe while wearing her necklace. Some parents opt to place the necklace around the baby's ankle and cover this with a sock to keep her pain free, rather than having her wear it around her neck.

Gum Massage

Another simple, yet effective remedy for teething pain is a gum massage. If your baby is fussing or in pain, place your clean finger in his mouth to feel for the area where the tooth is coming through. Massage this area by applying a small amount of pressure and moving your finger back and forth. Your baby may bite down on your finger to help apply even more pressure, and as long as this doesn't hurt you, it will help him to feel better!

Other Natural Teething Products to Try

There are many teething products on the market that can help relieve your baby's frustration as his body attempts to push through all those little teeth. Keep in mind that when looking for teething toys, you should opt for BPA-free toys or safe, wooden toys. Many plastic products contain toxic chemicals that can leach out into your baby's system as he chews. It is important that anything you give him to chew on is free from these toxins.

Many parents opt for natural wooden teethers; however, these may need to be coated with beeswax before use, so always refer to product instructions just to be sure. Always choose wooden teething toys that are coated with natural water-based sealants or food grade dyes. All soft teething toys should be made from safe silicone, rather than from latex or plastic.

Dental Care

With teeth coming through, your baby will need proper dental care to ensure her teeth are as healthy as can be. Look for BPA-free toothbrushes that fit on your finger. These have soft little projections that allow you to rub the teeth and remove plaque buildup. Do this daily to maintain healthy teeth. In addition, avoid letting your baby sleep with a bottle in her mouth. This is one of the leading causes of tooth decay in young children. Some pediatricians advise giving fluoride at this time but fluoride comes with its own set of issues, such as potential reduction in IQ (Choi et al., 2012). Overexposure to fluoride in the first eight years of life can cause the teeth to become severely discolored, a condition called fluorosis. In addition, fluorosis can result in the deposition of fluoride in hard and soft tissues of the body, causing crippling illness.

Since fluoride is commonly added to water in cities, as well as to some nursery water products, it is not difficult for a child to be overexposed. There is therefore no reason for anyone to drink fluoride. If you wish to use a very small amount to clean the teeth, wait until your child is old enough to spit it back out when you have finished brushing her teeth. The more you get your baby used to having her teeth brushed, the more amenable she will be to this procedure as she gets older. She may even love it. My youngest was the cutest thing when she rushed into the bathroom while I was brushing my teeth, asking me to brush hers as well. She was very independent and learned early about self-care, but still needed my help to make sure she cleaned in all the nooks and crannies.

Sleeping

According to the American Academy of Pediatrics, an infant of between four and eleven months in age should be sleeping an average of twelve to fifteen hours each day. At this stage, you may also notice your baby sleeping longer stretches at night. However, don't beat yourself up if your baby isn't sleeping for six-hour stretches at night. He may still be waking every few hours to feed and that's normal too. Feeding on demand, even at night, is still the best way to make sure your baby stays healthy and receives the nutrition he needs. This also triggers your milk supply to increase!

Nutrition

Some parents choose to start solids at four months, and others do not. While some babies can tolerate solids at this age, it is still very early and their sensitive stomachs may not be ready for this. It is completely normal to continue feeding breastmilk (or formula) exclusively at this time, as it has everything your baby needs to be healthy and to thrive. In fact, the consensus among medical institutions, such as the American Academy of Pediatrics, the U.S. National Institutes for Health, and the World Health Organization all agree that it is best to introduce solids at six months of age. Most babies are developmentally ready for solids at this time.

Nurturing Development

The ability to sit, unassisted, results when your baby's neck, back, and upper body muscles begin to strengthen. If you want to help encourage the strengthening of these important muscles, be sure to take plenty of stroller walks with your baby sitting in an upright position. You can nurture your baby's motor development at this time by giving her toys that she can grip easily and pass from one hand to the other. Try holding toys in front of your baby to see if she reaches out for them. If you think your baby is becoming more mobile at this stage, get ready for the six-to-nine month phase because your baby will no doubt start crawling then! Keep giving her plenty of tummy time to prepare her for this next phase of growth, muscle development, and mobility! Tummy time is the only thing that encourages a proper neck curvature. Babies can start doing this exercise right after they are born and it is amazing for their strength. Also, toys should not always be right in front of them but should be put off to one side, to encourage a range of motion in the neck.

Don't Eat That!

(Six to Nine Months)

Exploring the World of Food

That little personality is starting to show now! The six-to-nine month phase is full of fun discoveries, such as a baby's realization that he can easily get from one place to another or his attempts to communicate his desires with you more effectively. You're probably starting to get the hang of this parenting thing as well, and can differentiate between your baby's cries for attention and his cries for food. Speaking of food, your baby will likely be ready for solids at this time. He may also have perfected sitting unassisted. In this chapter, you will learn how to support your child during this phase by giving him superior nutrition with herbal snacks that he will love, as well as remedies for any skin issues he may develop as he experiences the world around him. Ear infections may start manifesting around this time as well. This chapter will also guide you on how to take care of these at home with remedies to keep your baby comfortable and infection-free.

Solids and Nutritious Herbal Snacks

From six months onwards, your baby may be ready to be introduced to solids. Each baby is different, and some may not be quite ready. Some signs that your baby is ready for solids include sitting unassisted, bringing objects to her mouth, opening her mouth when food is offered, fussing while watching you eat, grabbing for your food, and seeming hungry after nursing. If you think your baby is ready, start with one simple food at a time and avoid introducing multiple foods all at once so you can keep track of her reactions to each new food. This will help you determine if any foods cause stomach upset or allergic reactions. You can start with puréed foods, but my children have never cared for them and preferred to eat " big people's food" instead. If you do choose puréed foods, making them yourself is very easy and much healthier because you know exactly what is going into your baby's stomach.

Want to know a common myth that most parents and even doctors are still recommending? A great first food for babies is cereal. This is NOT true. The fact is, babies do not make enough of a digestive enzyme called amylase to digest the starch in grains until they are at least one year old. Cereal is probably one of the worst possible foods to feed your baby at this stage because it contains compounds that require amylase for proper digestion. The result of feeding cereal (which is often full of genetically modified grains anyway) is potential upset stomach and digestive issues. The fact is that many parents are told by pediatricians to give their babies cereal when this is not evidence-based information at all. Pediatricians may know about medical issues that arise in babies, but they do not receive much training in *nutrition*. To further illustrate this, a 2008 study showed that the amount of teaching time allocated to the field of nutrition in most medical schools is inadequate and many instructors expressed the need for additional instruction in nutritional issues (Adams et al., 2006).

So what are some ideal, evidence-based first foods that help to nourish and support your precious baby's growth?

I think sweet potatoes, mashed peas, green beans, or other soft veggies are best. It is NOT recommended that babies eat eggs, honey, or citrus fruit until the age of one. An allergy developed at this time can be an allergy for life, but if introduction of the food is delayed until the digestive system has matured, the allergy often does not develop. This is especially important if the allergy has shown up in other family members.

Other nutrition-packed first foods could include avocado, bone broth, or liver. With any food, it is best to introduce a very small amount and wait seventy-two hours to know whether or not the food will trigger an allergic reaction. Any food that is a choking hazard, such as nut butter, is to be avoided. Also save raw carrots and other hard veggies and hot dogs until babies have enough teeth to chew them.

The Vegan Baby

More and more people in today's world choose to follow a vegetarian or vegan diet. Most often this is for reasons of animal welfare and concern about the damage that livestock farming does to the planet. It is estimated that around 5% of North Americans are currently vegetarians (who eat plant foods along with eggs, dairy products and honey), and 4% are vegans (who exclude all animal products). While plant-based diets are known to carry considerable health benefits for adults, there have been very few scientific studies on the effects of vegan or vegetarian diets on babies and growing children. Plants do not contain all the nutrients that humans need and so parents will need to use supplements and fortified (enriched) foods if they are to provide all the essential ingredients for a child's body and brain growth.

If you would like your child to follow a vegan or vegetarian diet, the first thing you need to do is read the research and **make sure you are well informed**. According to studies, the most common deficiencies in these diets are in terms of protein, omega-3 fatty acids, iron, zinc, iodine, calcium, vitamin D, and vitamin B12 (Rudloff et al., 2019). These nutrients are crucial in healthy growth and development, and deficiencies can lead to life-long consequences such as stunted growth and reduced brain and nervous system capacities.

In the first few months of your baby's life, breast milk is ALL that is needed and, although this is an animal product, there is no ethical dilemma here. It is once you wish to introduce solids that careful planning has to be done. Soft veggies are the easiest foods to start with, as long as your baby is still getting protein from your breastmilk. When you wish to wean the baby then remember that the range of vegan milks, such as almond, soy or rice, have low protein levels and don't contain enough calcium or vitamin D to

be suitable for a growing baby. In terms of a cow's milk substitute, soy formula will probably be the only suitable option. Calcium and vitamin D are both needed to form strong bones and these two nutrients are often in short supply in a plant-based diet.

I breastfed both of my babies until they were two years old, and gave them nothing but breast milk until the age of six months. When they became old enough to learn to eat "big people's food," I simply mashed veggies from the table. And they'd try to eat the smashed veggies with their cute, chubby fingers.

The minerals iron and iodine are also not available in sufficient quantities in plant foods. Iron is essential for making red blood cells and iodine is needed for healthy neurological (brain) development. Both these minerals are found in animal products, mainly, so excluding eggs, meat, fish and dairy from the diet of a baby could have devastating consequences. Supplementation is essential and parents should seek the advice of a pediatrician or dietician on the choice of a suitable supplement.

Vitamin B12 is only found in animal products – it does not occur in

plants. And this vitamin, also known as cobalamin, is important for blood health and the development of nervous tissue (brain, again). This is the nutrient that is most likely to be deficient in a vegan mother who is breastfeeding, as well as in her infant. Many baby cereals are fortified with vitamin B, but it is still important to consider how you will ensure your baby gets enough of this vital nutrient. Also, although vegan and vegetarian children tend to have healthier levels of saturated fats in their bodies, there is one particular fatty acid that is not supplied by such a diet. The omega-3 fatty acid known as docosahexaenoic acid (DHA), is typically deficient in diets that do not include fish. This nutrient also influences neurological function in childhood, and will have to be supplemented in the diet of a vegan or vegetarian child (Kuratko et al., 2013).

The good news is that most government health agencies state that vegan and vegetarian diets are healthy for children, as long as supplementation takes place. Children on these diets need to be introduced to the high quality proteins in pulses, such as lentils, beans and peas, and to alternative protein sources such as tofu. The wider the variety of plant foods they eat, the greater their nutrient intake will be. This is sometimes easier said than done, as young children can be picky eaters and this limits the types of nutrients they ingest. Try not to give them fruit before they have finished their veggies, or you may find them turning up their noses at food that is not sweet.

And, at the end of the day, a vegan diet can be beneficial for children, preventing deficiencies in vitamin C and folate (vitamin B9), as well as reducing the risk of obesity, which can often persist into adulthood and lead to other, associated issues. In addition, an early vegan diet can protect against atherosclerosis (fat deposition in arteries), which starts in childhood when too much saturated fat is present in the diet (Sutter & Bender, 2021). Vegan and vegetarian children also get more polyunsaturated fats, fiber and healthy phytonutrients than children on an omnivorous diet.

Although you will have to plan your child's meals carefully and use fortified foods and supplements, it is perfectly possible to raise a child on a vegan or vegetarian diet. You must be aware of the potential risks in terms of brain and body development, and should seek the guidance of a pediatrician or dietician who is sympathetic to your choice of diet.

You can find further information regarding views on vegan and vegetarian diets for children by reading Garone (2020), and Hinde & Fairchild (2018). Check out these references on page 122 at the end, for the links.

Healthy Herbal Snacks

In addition to the nutrient-rich first foods mentioned, try the following herbal recipes to replace unhealthy, processed, and sugar-filled snacks.

Lavender Marshmallows

Marshmallow root (*Althaea officinalis*) is a medicinal herb used traditionally for coating a sore throat or lubricating the intestines to relieve inflammation. Marshmallow root also has a history of use in sweets, and is responsible for the original marshmallows that we now roast around a campfire. Of course, today's marshmallows are not made with the root anymore, but rather with processed sugars and gelatin. However, you can still utilize this mucilaginous herbal root to make old-fashioned marshmallow snacks for your little one. You can even add flavorful herbs that double as powerful soothing agents for her.

Follow the recipe below for old-fashioned marshmallows made with marshmallow root and lavender. My grandmother taught me how to make these when I was little and had a craving for something sweet. These make an excellent natural snack for a little one in need of calming or soothing for a sore throat. Keep in mind that any kind of sugar (even sugar from fruit juice) is not good for babies and thus should be limited. Do not allow your child to have more than one marshmallow square daily:

Ingredients:

- 2 TBSP organic dried, powdered marshmallow root
- 2 cups distilled water
- 4 TBSP lavender buds
- 1 cup organic apple juice
- 4 TBSP organic gelatin powder

Instructions:

1. Place the marshmallow root and one cup of distilled water in a sterile jar to sit in the refrigerator overnight.

2. The next day, boil one cup of water with the lavender buds for fifteen minutes and then strain it out.

3. Pour the infused lavender water into a double boiler and let this boil until it is reduced by half.

4. When the liquid is reduced by half, blend in an equal amount of organic apple juice and set aside.

5. Strain the marshmallow root from the refrigerated infusion.

6. In a large bowl, blend one half cup of the strained marshmallow root infusion with four TBSP gelatin.

7. In a small pot, mix together the other half cup of marshmallow infusion (you may have to top it up with more distilled water) and a splash of apple juice.

8. Heat the juice and marshmallow infusion on medium heat until it begins to boil, then lower the heat and let this simmer while stirring constantly for ten minutes.

9. Pour the juice and marshmallow blend in with the gelatin and use

a hand mixer to beat for up to ten minutes, or until you see stiff peaks developing.

10. Blend in the lavender and juice mixture from step 3 and 4, mixing slowly.

11. Spread this on a baking sheet covered in parchment paper and refrigerate for several hours. Cut it into small squares and enjoy.

Delicious & Calming Herbal Popsicles

If the summer heat has your baby fussing, you can make delicious herbal popsicles that both cool her down while calming and soothing at the same time. You can substitute chamomile, linden blossom, or lavender for lemon balm in this recipe, if you wish. Each of these herbs has gentle, calming properties that can help to soothe and pacify your baby.

Instructions:

1. Boil four tablespoons of lemon balm with two cups of water on the stove for ten minutes.

2. Strain out plant material and add

one cup of the organic fruit juice of your choice.

3. Pour this into popsicle molds.

4. Freeze overnight.

5. Let your baby enjoy these with your supervision.

Skin Care

You may begin to notice that your baby's sensitive skin reacts to various surfaces, detergents, and other substances as she becomes more mobile and rolls around on the carpet and floor. Keep your baby's body covered, as much as possible, to prevent rug burns on the knees and elbows. Some carpets and floorings contain toxic chemicals that can irritate a baby's skin, as do many detergents. You should already be using a child-safe detergent to wash your baby's clothes, but if you notice rashes and irritation where clothing was rubbing, consider opting for a detergent that is free of all fragrances and dyes. These are two major culprits when it comes to skin issues in babies. To soothe rashes, first try the calendula salve recipe mentioned earlier in this book. You can also try the herbal salve recipe below, for soothing and cooling red, irritated rashes:

Simple Chickweed Salve

Chickweed (*Stellaria media*) is a very common cool-weather "weed" that grows prolifically in most yards during the spring and fall months. It can quickly cool down heat rashes and irritated patches of skin. You can make a quick salve with this by collecting it and wilting it on a towel overnight. While chickweed is best used as fresh as possible, it is inadvisable to use it fresh when making a salve, as you increase that mold will develop in the preparation. Wilting it overnight is sufficient to remove most of the water content and thus create an effective salve.

Fill a sterile glass jar with wilted chickweed and completely cover this in melted coconut oil. Place this jar in a pan of hot water and follow the coconut oil salve recipe to create this chickweed salve. Use it as needed by applying a liberal amount to dry skin, skin rashes, and red or irritated areas of skin.

Aloe Vera Eczema Remedy

Many parents complain that eczema is an issue with their little one's skin. While eczema has many causes, one of the biggest culprits isn't what the skin is exposed to, but rather what is in the diet. Before trying an herbal remedy for eczema, try cutting out known eczema triggers like dairy, gluten, citrus fruits and other acidic foods, and processed foods. If you still notice eczema patches, try making a soothing lavender gel to apply to the area.

Start by blending one half cup of food grade aloe vera gel with one tablespoon of lavender-infused jojoba oil (see oil infusion recipe earlier in this book). Aloe vera is one of the best anti-inflammatory and soothing herbs available. Lavender is great for soothing skin and reducing irritation. Together, they help tame and reduce symptoms of eczema. Store this in the refrigerator between uses, and blend well before each application.

Bug Bite and Sting Stick

It is inevitable that, as much as you try to shield your precious little one, he will eventually experience a bug bite or sting. Some children don't react much to a bite or sting, while others experience severely inflamed areas that appear red and itchy. I have always had pretty bad reactions to bug bites and we have so many mosquitoes where I live. Unfortunately, my kids react to bites like I do. Consider creating this powerful remedy in the spring to have on hand during the summer months when bug bites and stings are more common:

Ingredients:

- ½ cup of lavender-infused oil (lavender is very soothing to skin and can help it heal)

- ½ cup of dried broadleaf plantain-infused oil (plantain has been used for centuries to treat bug bites, stings, and skin irritations, and is found regularly in yards)

- One ounce (30 g) of beeswax pellets

Instructions:

1. To make the lavender infusion and the broadleaf plantain infusion, go back to the section on "Macerated Oils" for instructions (Page 21).

2. Follow the recipe for making salve given earlier in the book –this details how to make a salve with beeswax, using a double boiler.

3. Pour this into tins to cool, and consider pouring some into empty lip balm containers for easier application to bites and stings.

4. Store this in a cool, dark place

because it can melt if left in a hot area for too long.

Ear Infections

Ear infections are no fun. The first time your baby starts to get a little congested, she may develop an ear infection because her ear canals aren't as developed as those of an older child or adult. Mucus and germs can get stuck in a baby's ears and fester there, causing an infection. One of my children had many ear infections as a baby. It is a very scary thing for any parent. But there are ways to treat them if they do happen. First, be on watch for an ear infection at the first sign of congestion or a runny nose. Then, monitor your baby for fussiness, tugging at the ears, red ears, and fluid coming from the ears. As a result of the infection, your baby may also run a fever. To help treat the pain and inflammation, as well as the infection itself, you can try the two remedies below. Make sure to administer them at the first suspicion of an infection for best results.

Mullein Flower and Garlic Ear Oil

Garlic Ear Oil

Mullein (*Verbascum thapsus*) flowers are an excellent remedy for pain and inflammation in the ear, caused by infection. Garlic is one of the most potent natural antibiotics, and an excellent remedy to blend with mullein flowers to help tackle an ear infection. You can create ear oil for your little one by following the steps below.

Ingredients:

- 2 TBSP mullein flowers
- 2 TBSP chopped garlic cloves
- Enough olive oil to completely cover the garlic and mullein

Instructions:

1. Fill a sterile glass jar with the chopped garlic and mullein flowers.

2. Cover the plant material completely in olive oil.

3. Cover the jar with a cheesecloth that is secured with a rubber band or string.

4. Place this jar in a pan of hot water, on low heat, for eight to ten hours (or longer if you wish) and then remove it from heat and strain it. Bottle the oil and let it cool. Store it in the refrigerator between uses, to preserve freshness. This preparation should last for up to three months in the refrigerator.

5. Gently warm the oil before using it by sitting it in a pan of warm water.

6. Apply five drops in the ear canal and place a cotton ball at the outer end of the canal to keep the oil from leaking out. Have your child lie on her side and allow the oil to contact the infected ear drum for ten to fifteen minutes. Apply this ear oil, at the first sign of infection, up to three times daily for best results.

Oregano-Infused Oil for Lymphatic Massage

Oregano (*Origanum vulgare*) is another potent antibiotic herb. Instead of reaching for oregano essential oil, which is highly concentrated and could cause damage to your little one's skin, opt for oregano-infused olive oil instead. This is much gentler and is made by following the herbal oil infusion protocol given in the first part of the book. After you have infused oregano into olive oil, massage this into the skin around the ear and down the neck, below the ears. Never place this inside the ear canal. You can help encourage lymph to flow more freely by massaging this oil down the neck, on either side, for several minutes each day. This can also help tackle infection in the area while simultaneously promoting drainage of the ear canal to minimize infection.

If your child has congestion, along with the ear infection symptoms, it is highly recommended that you visit a chiropractor as soon as possible (no matter the child's age) to adjust and help with drainage.

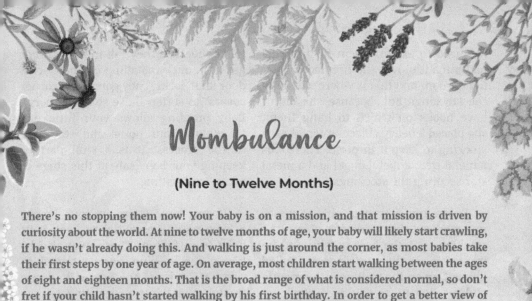

Mombulance

(Nine to Twelve Months)

There's no stopping them now! Your baby is on a mission, and that mission is driven by curiosity about the world. At nine to twelve months of age, your baby will likely start crawling, if he wasn't already doing this. And walking is just around the corner, as most babies take their first steps by one year of age. On average, most children start walking between the ages of eight and eighteen months. That is the broad range of what is considered normal, so don't fret if your child hasn't started walking by his first birthday. In order to get a better view of once forbidden territory, your child may start pulling himself up on objects. This allows him to stand upright and helps strengthen his leg muscles to get them ready for walking. Just make sure to keep an eye on him, as he may try to pull himself up on just about anything! The nine to twelve month phase is one in which you will definitely need to be ready to intervene, if necessary, because accidents can and will happen. In this chapter, you will learn how to create your own herbal first aid kit to treat minor cuts, scrapes, burns, and other irritations that may occur in this phase in your child's life.

My nephew was in this age range when he started becoming more mobile. It happened to be Christmas time and my sister had her usual over-the-top decorations on display around the house. All these decorations look pretty awesome to a little one and, naturally, most feel the need to explore them further. She had a mantle over the fireplace in her living room and this is where she hung the stockings but, because she didn't have hooks on which to hang them, she placed a heavy object on top of each stocking to keep it in place. There was a metal tree, a metal angel and a metal star securing the stockings.

Before my sister was able to get to my nephew, his curiosity about the stockings got the best of him and he wanted to see them up close. He pulled himself up on the wall near the mantle and reached up to tug on a stocking. I will spare you the graphic detail, but a metal Christmas tree came down on his head as he tugged that stocking. He was fine but needed a few stitches in the emergency room. Head wounds sometimes look worse than they really are because they bleed a lot. He was covered in blood and my sister is still traumatized by that day. She now has another little one and is much more mindful of accidents that can happen when certain objects are within a baby's reach.

Baby Proofing

When your baby reaches this stage, take some time to walk around your house and think about what could happen if she were to mess with this or that. Don't underestimate her curiosity! If it is even remotely within her reach, there is a good chance she will want to touch or grab it. Some common things to take into consideration when making sure your house is safe for your baby include covering electrical outlets (yes, babies have attempted to stick things in the holes), purchasing a toilet lock (babies have drowned in toilets because they fall in and cannot get back out), installing cabinet locks, door knob locks, baby gates, and corner covers (to soften those sharp corners). Baby proofing allows your little one to explore your home and stay safe in the process. It is a vital part of keeping your baby safe at this stage of active exploration.

If you have stairs in your house, a baby gate is essential to keep your baby from falling. These may also be handy for keeping her contained in one, safe room of the house. Be aware though, that while a security gate may look impenetrable, some toddlers have figured out how to open them; make sure you don't leave your little one unattended in a room where a gate is keeping her safe. If you find yourself needing to step away for a second, consider placing your baby in a play pen with large, sturdy walls that she can't crawl over. The best way to ensure her safety, however, is to bring her with you if you have to step out of the room.

You will likely need to make sure your trash can lid is secured. Nobody wants to find a baby playing in trash, some of which could cause illness, if ingested. In addition, furniture straps are a must. Since many little ones attempt climbing at this stage (or shortly after), now is the time for you to secure heavy furniture like dressers, televisions, television stands, and wardrobes to the wall. Many tragic accidents have occurred when children attempt to climb up onto these pieces of furniture which then fall over on top of them.

Consider also using stove knob protectors if your stove has knobs that a baby can reach. A sliding door lock, and other devices to keep your baby from opening doors, are also recommended. Keep some of these with you when traveling , as well, to baby proof your hotel room. Keep any and all medications and medicines out of reach of your little one. Lock your medicine cabinet. Be mindful of all potentially poisonous and hazardous substances in your house, such as bleach, cleaning supplies, insecticides, and other chemicals. Store them in a locked cabinet. Remember that even if your baby were to get to these and not ingest them, simple exposure to the extra-sensitive skin could result in some serious reactions.

A baby likes the cause-and-effect actions in this phase. He may start wanting to help you turn lights on and off as you leave and enter rooms. This is fine, but if he figures out how to do this on his own, and can reach, you can purchase light switch protectors to thwart him. This cause-and-effect action is not limited to the light switches. It isn't hard for a baby to learn how to turn on and off faucets. This can be extremely dangerous if the hot water is turned on. Set your water heater temperature to a level that cannot burn your child, if he were to turn on the hot water. Consider using anti-scald devices for faucets and shower heads, as well.

Herbal First Aid Kit

We have all seen the typical first aid kits people use in the event of an accident. They usually consist of wound care treatments, fever reducers, pain relievers, and antihistamines. While having a first aid kit is very important, it is entirely possible to swap out some

of those products with natural products that can do the same thing, but without the chemicals. For example, some kits contain triple antibiotic ointment: this consists of antibiotics mixed with a substance that makes it easy to apply to wounds. Firstly, antibiotics aren't needed unless an infection already exists; a simple antiseptic will help clean an initial wound. But also, did you know that the substance used to suspend the antibiotics is actually a derivative of oil refining? That's right. Petroleum jelly, the base of many commercial ointments and chest rubs, is a nasty by-product of the oil refining process. There are much better substances you can put on your child's skin! In this section, you will learn how to create your own natural products to treat the various cuts, scrapes, burns, and bites you may encounter.

Yarrow is Your Friend

When it comes to wounds, yarrow is one of the best herbs to utilize. Yarrow is a very common plant that is widespread throughout most of North America and Europe. It is a plant full of legend and lore. It is said that the great Greek warrior Achilles used this plant to help soldiers on the battlefield. This is how yarrow got the Latin name, *"Achillea" millefolium*. *Millefolium* means "a thousand leaves," which is fitting for this plant because its leaves have a fern-like appearance with many little projections. Yarrow can help to staunch blood flow and make a wound clot more quickly. It is also naturally antiseptic, so it helps to kill bacteria that may have entered the wound. Finally, it is incredibly healing to the skin and surrounding tissues. There are several products you can make with yarrow, so be sure to add this invaluable plant to your herbal first aid kit.

Yarrow Styptic Powder

This is one of the easiest products you can make with yarrow, yet it is incredibly useful and effective. Since yarrow naturally helps staunch blood flow, people often crush it and apply it to wounds. It is often an abundant and readily-available remedy growing in the fields in the summer months. While crushing yarrow leaves between your fingers and applying this paste to the wound does help, you can make your own powder with yarrow that works even more effectively. All you need is dried yarrow leaves, along with a mortar and pestle. When the leaves are nice and crispy-dry, place them in the mortar and grind this up with the pestle until you have a powder-like consistency. Store this powder in

a sterile glass jar and keep it in a cool, dark place until you need it. When someone experiences a cut, scrape, or scratch, apply the powder to the area and let it sit to promote healing.

Yarrow Salve

Yarrow can also be infused into a skin-nourishing oil to make a salve. A salve comes in handy for treating wounds daily, until they heal. It can be applied as often as needed to speed up the healing process, while keeping infection at bay. You can make a simple salve with dried yarrow leaves and flowers by infusing them in coconut oil and following the salve-making protocol given earlier in this book. Store your salve in a sterile tin or glass jar and keep it in a cool, dark place to use, as needed, on wounds, bites, and rashes to help them heal.

One more thing about yarrow ... bugs hate it. There is something about yarrow that makes bugs avoid it in the wild. When collecting wild yarrow, it is uncommon to find any bugs on the plant. It produces pungent plant oils that work to repel pests. This makes it doubly valuable to a parent because it can be applied before a child goes outdoors and will repel pests, while at the same time keeping the skin healthy and nourished.

Burn Remedies

The sun is a good thing because it helps our bodies make vitamin D, but everything in moderation! Your little one's sensitive skin may burn more easily than your adult skin if she is allowed out in the sun for too long. First, make sure to cover your little one's body with clothing as much as possible, if you are going outdoors for an extended time. This is an infinitely better strategy than smearing her up with sunscreens that may do more harm than good – many are full of carcinogenic and hormone-disrupting chemicals. Sun protective clothing is a simple and natural way to protect your little one from the sun, rather than using sunscreen. Make sure to put a good hat on her head as well, one that shades the back of her neck, face, and ears. These little areas are often neglected and can become burned easily. If your baby does experience sunburn, there are some remedies below that you can use to ease pain, redness, and inflammation. These remedies are also great for accidental burns around the house.

Aloe Vera Cooling Burn Treatment

Every household should have at least one *Aloe vera* plant. Why? These plants are extremely easy to grow and have excellent medicinal properties. The gel inside the leaves of the plant is highly anti-inflammatory, cooling, and antiseptic. It is very soothing to red, irritated skin. You can help treat your child's skin irritations by simply plucking a leaf off and scraping out that inner gel. Apply this to the burn as often

as needed to help soothe and relieve pain while also promoting healing of the affected skin.

Chickweed The Burn "Weed"

After aloe vera, Chickweed (*Stellaria media*) is one of the best plants for burns. This is because it is known for its cooling and skin-nourishing properties. It is a very common plant in yards during the spring and fall months but because it is small and inconspicuous you might not find it unless you are looking for it. This is one herbal remedy that is best made with plant matter that is fresh. Simply make a poultice by crushing the plant up and applying it to the burn. After an hour, you can crush more up and reapply it fresh, to keep the area cool while helping skin to recover.

Burn Remedy Combo

If you are able to procure both chickweed and aloe vera, you can create a cooling spray to treat burns with ease. This spray combines these powerful plants to help expedite healing for burns, bites, and other wounds. The best part is how easy it is to apply! No need to apply any pressure to an already painful area when you are able to use a spray.

Instructions:

1. Boil one cup of water and add three tablespoons of fresh chickweed.

2. Remove this from heat.

3. Allow it to infuse with a lid covering it for fifteen to twenty minutes.

4. Strain out the liquid and blend in two to three tablespoons of aloe vera gel.

5. Place this in a spray bottle and shake it well to make sure the aloe vera has blended well.

6. Allow this to cool completely before using.

7. Store it in the refrigerator between uses. Storage in the refrigerator also helps to keep the liquid cool,

for additional skin relief when it is applied.

8. Spray on burns and other wounds as often as needed.

9. Discard after twenty-four hours.

Other Ideas

The calendula salve recipe mentioned earlier in this book, as well as the bug bite and sting stick recipe detailed in the previous chapter, make excellent additions to an herbal first aid kit as well. For more useful remedies to add to your kit, see the "Antihistamine Remedy" in the following chapter, as well as recipes for treating coughing, congestion, fevers, and viruses. Keep all of these on hand so they are ready when you need them.

Weeble Wobble, Don't Fall Now

(One to Two Years Old)

I vividly remember my son's first birthday. It was an outdoor, nautical-themed party at our lake house, with views of the placid water all around us. The house is on a peninsula, so the yard is surrounded on three sides by water. We were still learning as parents, but it didn't take long for us to realize that a bunch of toddlers running around on a peninsula surrounded by water wasn't the best idea! What a crazy day! That first year was so intense, with us learning how to meet our son's needs and struggling through sleepless nights, teething, tantrums … and the list goes on . This probably won't be the case with everyone reading this, but my son seemed to experience a personality shift around twelve months of age. This shift made our lives, as his parents, easier. So I wanted to celebrate with an over-the-top birthday party.

Things change for many children at this stage simply because they are more mobile. Mobility creates a need to explore and be free. The constant desire to be in Mom's arms is replaced by the need to explore the enormous world around them. As your baby grows, this will happen little by little, with each child displaying different tendencies. Around one year of age, your baby will likely start taking his first steps and after that, full-on walking isn't far behind. Communication is getting easier at this point too, because your baby has figured out how to let you know when he needs or wants something specific. He may start out saying one word here and there, but by the age of two will be able to speak in simple sentences. With more exposure, your child will likely get sick from time to time as his immune system learns how to fight off invaders. In this chapter, you will learn how to guide your child through this phase in physical, mental, and social development, as well as how to take care of your little one as he experiences sicknesses like viruses and congestion.

Physical Development

There is no need to panic if your little one is not walking by her first birthday. Every child is different, with some waiting several months past this point before they start walking. Each one of my children experienced milestones at different times. My first child actually took her first steps at about fifteen months, walking to my best friend Jes while chasing an Oreo cookie. My youngest took off at about eleven months and hasn't stopped since. Your baby should at least be crawling and pulling herself up on things at this stage. This is called "cruising." She may even take a few steps without holding onto anything. Babies often start standing alone at around one year of age, meaning that they can pose for a cute photo ... if you're fast! By the time your little one is two years old, whe should be walking and running, as well as climbing, kicking balls, walking up and down stairs while holding a rail, throwing a ball overhand, and standing on tiptoes. Keep in mind that these are based on averages, but if you aren't seeing the physical development you expect at this time, it never hurts to talk to your pediatrician.

Look for fine motor development to change in this phase as well. The little muscles in your child's hands are strengthening and you may find that in addition to picking up a spoon and feeding herself, she is able to draw objects like circles and lines more easily. Nurture this by giving your little one plenty of time to be crafty. Give her kid-safe paint and paper and ask her to copy or trace the circles and lines you draw. You can also help build fine motor skills by having her put toys into a container and take them out again.

Mental Development

Life is becoming more fun for your baby as he realizes that something will happen as a result of his actions. This fun cause-and-effect phenomenon could include the loud noise that occurs when banging together pots and pans, or an agitated "meow" from the cat when poked or prodded. Your child might be able to follow simple directions because, at this stage, he understands more than he is able to articulate. Many children understand what you are asking if you tell them to do something simple, such as "pick up this toy." Nurture his mental development, as well as his ability to learn language skills, by reading to your child as much as possible. It is never too early to read to children, even from the moment they are born! One of my fondest memories growing up is curling up in my mom's lap as she read aloud everything from the newspapers to her reader's digest condensed books. Because of this practice, I too became an avid reader.

Social Development

When your child was still an infant, you may have attempted to get together with other moms to let your children have a playdate. At this stage, your children likely played *near* each other, but not *with* each other. This is called Parallel Play. Eventually, you will start to notice your child interacting with other children and participating in more social play. She may start to include other children in chase games or hide and seek-style games. As her social skills develop, she may start getting excited when it is time to play with another child or copy the actions of older children. Both of my older children have become annoyed at the younger ones for copying their behaviors or preferences. I often have to remind them that they did the same to me until they found their own way of doing things. This mimicking of behavior is important for their development. Nurture your child's social development by joining local "mommy and me" groups or scheduling play dates with other children of the same age.

Sickness is Inevitable

Being sick is a part of life. We have all been sick in the past. As scary as it may seem the first time your little one is running a fever or sounding congested, remember that this is a way for her immune system to "learn" how to defeat viruses and other invaders. Your child's immune system grows stronger with each virus or pathogen it encounters. The next time your child crosses paths with the same virus, her immune system will recall how to fight that pathogen, and this will decrease or eliminate symptoms altogether.

When your little one is under the weather, your priority should be to keep her comfortable and hydrated. Dehydration is one of the leading causes for hospitalizations of children, so it is crucial to make sure they are getting the fluids they need. However, don't expect them to be ravenously thirsty as they fight an illness. This refusal to drink fluids happens when many children are sick, but you can take sneaky steps to keep them hydrated. These steps can include giving them herbal popsicles periodically, or even super hydrating fruit or veggies like watermelon or cucumber. If you are especially worried about your child staying hydrated, you can also fill a medicine syringe with water every twenty to thirty minutes and put it in her mouth.

Remedies for Viruses

After one year of age, your child can be introduced safely to more foods and medicinal herbs. Continue introducing one herb at a time just to be safe. The remedies below can help your child by giving the immune system what it needs to function optimally so that it can fight viruses. Viruses cause colds, flu and other types of illnesses.

Elderberry Glycerite

Elderberry (*Sambucus* spp.) is an immunomodulatory remedy, meaning it can help nourish the immune system by encouraging it to function properly as the body fights a virus. Elderberries are an excellent source of quercetin, so they also help fight inflammatory histamines that cause allergies. You can make a syrup for your little one that he will take without a fight because it is delicious! Using the glycerite-making protocol:

1. Create a glycerite with dehydrated elderberries.

   a. If you use fresh elderberries, do not add any water to your glycerite during the process.

2. Before you are ready to strain out your elderberry glycerite, add some heat by placing your jar into a pot of water on the stove.

3. Cook this over low heat for five to six hours. Elderberry is one of several plant remedies that requires heat to increase potency.

4. While cooking your remedy, add a few sticks of cinnamon, cloves (*Syzygium aromaticum*), and sliced ginger root, if you wish. These help make your remedy even more effective for fighting a virus.

5. Let this cool and then strain it through a cheesecloth into a sterile glass jar.

6. Squeeze the cheesecloth well to get all the glycerin out of the berries.

7. Using a funnel during this process will help prevent spills.

8. Give your child five milliliters every three hours (during the daytime) at the first sign of illness. Continue giving this until your child is better.

9. You can easily store it in the refrigerator for up to 18 months

If you (or another family member) come down with something, you can start taking this to prevent sickness in the remaining family members. Adults can take ten to fifteen milliliters, two to three times daily for prevention, and children can take five milliliters, two to three times a day, for prevention.

Elderberry Syrup

You can also make this elderberry syrup to help treat viral infections.

Ingredients:

- 1 cup of elderberries
- 3 cups of water
- 1 inch of ginger
- 1 tsp ground cloves
- 2 cinnamon sticks

Instructions:

1. In a sauce pot on the stove, combine all the ingredients.

2. Bring to a boil then simmer until liquid is reduced by half.

3. Cool and strain with cheesecloth.

4. Combine with honey to sweeten as much as you'd like.

5. Take as directed above.

I personally love adding extra herbs for different uses, such as extra immunity boosting herbs or allergy reducing herbs. Be sure to do the scratch tests before adding extra herbs to any remedy.

Shikimic Acid Remedy

Years ago, scientists discovered a compound in star anise (*Illicium verum*) that could be used to fight viruses. In their search for more sustainable plants that contain this compound they also discovered it in unripe, sweetgum tree balls (fruits) and pine needles . The compound is called shikimic acid. In a lab, shikimic acid was extracted from the plants and then used to create the popular influenza prescription called Tamiflu. However, this medication to shorten the duration of a virus has many side effects, such as hearing voices and experiencing strange mood changes. It can also cause headaches, pain, vomiting, and insomnia, among other things. You can skip the lab-altered remedy by making your own antiviral extract at home using pine (*Pinus*) needles, star anise, or unripe, sweetgum balls from the sweetgum tree (*Liquidambar styraciflua*). Around here, pine trees are everywhere, and we also have a lot of sweetgum trees. Star anise can be found online or in many stores. This remedy won't have the unwanted side effects that its lab-altered relative possesses.

Instructions: (Feel free to play around with the proportions of plant material depending on what you can find readily available between the three shikimic acid-containing plants. You can even add a little of each plant to the jar.)

1. Fill a sterile glass jar with star anise, pine needles, or chopped sweetgum balls.

2. Completely cover these in non-GMO vegetable glycerin.

3. Add a splash of distilled water to fill the jar up to the top before putting the lid on it.

4. Store it in a cool, dark place for four to six weeks, shaking the jar daily.

5. Strain this through a cheesecloth when it is ready.

6. Store it in a sterile glass jar in the refrigerator, for up to three years; it can also be stored for up to two years in a cabinet.

7. Give your child ten drops up to three times daily, if you feel that she is coming down with a virus (especially if you think she has influenza).

8. Adults can take five to ten millimeters of this extract, three times daily, to fight a virus.

Rose Hip Syrup to Fight Viruses

Rose hips (*Rosa canina*), which are the fruits of rose plants, are high in vitamin C; they contain more vitamin C than most other plant sources. In addition, these little fruits left behind on rose bushes in the fall have a pleasant flavor. They can be infused in hot water to make a tasty, vitamin C-rich syrup that children will love. This vitamin is essential for healthy immune function and can be given, along with elderberries, when your child is under the weather.

Instructions:

1. Bring one cup of water to a boil.

2. Pour this over one half cup of rose hips in a jar. I use crushed whole rose hips to brew my tea.

3. Tighten the lid and allow this to steep for several hours.

4. Just filter well to be sure no irritating hairs remain.

5. Strain out the liquid and add one cup of raw honey. *Be sure not to give honey to anyone less than one year old.*

6. Blend this well

7. Give your child five to ten milliliters as needed when he has a virus.

8. Store honey-based syrups that are NOT canned or frozen in the refrigerator for up to six months.

Pine Syrup

Pine serves two useful purposes when someone is suffering from a virus. First, it is a great source of vitamin C, so it can help nourish the immune system to help fight off the virus. Second, it is a great remedy for respiratory support, especially for children who have an upper respiratory virus. You can make a tasty syrup with pine needles. This is also one of the only remedies for lower respiratory congestion.

Ingredients:

• One cup of water

• ½ cup of chopped pine needles

Instructions:

1. Boil the water on the stove top.

2. Add the needles, reduce heat to a simmer, and let this infuse for several hours with the lid on.

3. Strain out the liquid and add one cup of raw honey.

4. Blend this well and store it in the refrigerator, between uses, for one to six months. Give your child five to ten milliliters, as needed, for viruses, coughs, and other respiratory issues.

Some varieties of pine are NOT safe to ingest. Ponderosa pine (*Pinus ponderosa*), yew (*Taxus baccata*), Australian pine (*Casuarina equisetifolia*), hemlock (*Conium maculatum*) and Norfolk Island pine (*Araucaria heterophylla*) are poisonous. RESEARCH your pine before making this remedy, if you are foraging. If you are just starting out you can buy cleaned and correctly-chosen pine needles online, to make things easier.

Remedies for Cough, Congestion, and Croup

It is rough for parents to hear their little ones coughing all night. There are remedies that can soothe your little one's sore throat, ease his cough, and help him breathe more peacefully, day or night. Try one of the recipes below for respiratory complaints.

Mullein and Sage Syrup

Mullein (*Verbascum thapsus*) is one of the best plants for helping to open up the bronchial area, thus easing coughing, and promoting healthy breathing. It is a very common plant throughout most of the world and may just be in your backyard right now! It has large leaves, arranged in a basal rosette, that are known for their furry texture. Sage (*Salvia officinalis*) is another great plant for helping to soothe a sore throat, kill harmful bacteria, and ease spasmodic coughing. When combined, these herbs create a wonderful remedy to tackle coughing, sore throats, and respiratory issues. To make soothing syrup with these plants, follow the recipe below.

Ingredients:

* One tablespoon of each plant (dried and chopped)
* Two cups of water

Instructions:

1. Start by boiling the water on the stove.

2. Add herbs and reduce to a simmer.

3. Let the water reduce by half and then remove this from heat.

4. Strain out the liquid and pour it into a sterile glass jar.

5. Pour one cup of raw honey into the jar, making sure to blend it well.

6. Keep this in the refrigerator to use, as needed, for up to a month.

7. Give your child five to ten milliliters every two to three hours for a cough, sore throat, or congestion.

Thyme and Ginger Sinuses Oxymel

Thyme (*Thymus vulgaris*) is an excellent herb for killing harmful bacteria. It is highly antimicrobial and antibacterial due to the presence of potent compounds like thymol. Thyme has been used historically to soothe a sore throat, kill harmful bacteria in the throat, and open up the sinuses and respiratory tract. Ginger is also highly anti-inflammatory, and can help bring down swelling that may be causing soreness, pain, and difficulty with breathing. You can combine these two herbs to make an oxymel for treating coughing and congestion. An oxymel is simply an herbal remedy that combines organic apple cider vinegar with raw honey. Both apple cider vinegar and raw honey are amazing cough and sore throat remedies on their own, but when combined with thyme and ginger, this remedy really knocks out congestion.

Instructions:

1. Fill a jar with one part chopped thyme and one part chopped ginger.

2. Cover three-quarters of the plant material in the jar with raw honey.

3. Top it off with raw organic apple cider vinegar until everything is completely covered.

4. Shake this well and store the jar in a cool, dark place for four weeks.

5. Shake the jar daily and top it up with more honey or apple cider vinegar if you notice the plant material is exposed at the top.

6. Strain this out through a cheesecloth after four weeks, and bottle it in a sterile glass jar.

7. Keep this in the refrigerator between uses; it should last for three to four months.

8. Give your child five milliliters, every three hours, as needed for a cough and congestion.

Mullein Tea for Asthma

Mullein leaves are a great remedy for opening the airways and relieving inflammation and congestion that worsen conditions like asthma. Mullein is a respiratory tonic and helps to rid the body of excess mucus as well. It is also excellent for reducing swollen nasal tissue, making it easier to drain mucus-filled sinuses.

Instructions:

1. Infuse two teaspoons of mullein leaves into one cup of hot water for ten minutes.

2. Add raw honey for a better taste.

3. Allow this to cool a bit before giving it to your child.

4. Have your child drink one cup daily for respiratory support.

Remedies for Fever

First of all, a fever is a good thing. Yes, a fever may look and sound scary, but it is the body's way of getting the better of a virus or infection by heating itself to make an inhospitable environment for the unwanted pathogen. According to Dr. Diane Arnaout, a pediatrician, the extra warmth makes it difficult for the pathogen to replicate quickly. Instead, it begins to break down altogether, which slows its spread significantly. After a while, a fever will defeat the germ, thanks to the wonderful way in which our immune system works! We have been trained by some well-meaning doctors to treat a fever and keep it down by rotating all kinds of over-the-counter pain relievers and fever reducers. What we are actually doing is potentially prolonging the life of the virus in our bodies and preventing our immune system from doing its job.

There are times when a fever may need treatment, but then it should be 102°F (39°C) or higher for children of three months or older. Additionally, if a fever lasts for more than four to five days, or is in a child under three months of age, this is a time to seek help for the fever. Children with neurologic conditions also need to be monitored closely, as their brains cannot regulate fever like the brains of other children. Below are some remedies to help reduce a fever if you are concerned that your child's temperature is getting too high. Just remember that a fever is a good thing in most cases and only treat it if absolutely necessary.

Yarrow Tea

We know yarrow is a wonderful herb for treating wounds, but it is also a great febrifuge (a medicine used to reduce fever). It can help induce sweating in order to lower a fever. You can make a tea with yarrow by infusing one to two teaspoons of dried yarrow leaves or flowers into one cup of hot water for ten to fifteen minutes. Add a bit of raw honey to improve taste and give your child small doses of this – approximately one ounce (30 g) every few hours – throughout the day. Store it in the refrigerator between uses.

Peppermint Bath

Another great remedy for a fever is a tepid bath infused with peppermint leaves. Fill a muslin drawstring bag with a half cup of peppermint leaves and let this infuse in the bath as you are running the water. Sit your child in the bath for as long as you wish. Peppermint is naturally cooling and an effective febrifuge. The tepid water will also work to bring the body temperature down.

Anemia

Some viruses and respiratory infections can lead to anemia. Anemia occurs when the blood doesn't have enough red blood cells or hemoglobin to help transport oxygen where it is needed. It is important to make sure your child is getting enough iron in her diet if she has issues with anemia. Iron plays an important role in helping to oxygenate the red blood cells and it also helps maintain a healthy immune system. The remedy below can help give your child the iron she needs to be healthy.

Nettle Tea

Stinging nettle contains high amounts of iron, which can significantly help with anemia. It is also rich in other nutrients, such as vitamins A, B, C, and K. The presence of these essential vitamins helps the body to absorb iron better. This blood–building plant is perfect in tea or bone broth for children who are anemic.

Instructions:

1. Infuse two teaspoons of dried stinging nettle leaves into one cup of hot water for fifteen minutes.

2. Add raw honey to taste and have your child drink one to two cups daily.

   Or

1. Boil two tablespoons of stinging nettle leaves into a liter of bone broth.

2. Give your child one cup of this weekly to build nutrient and iron levels.

Pink eye

Pink eye is an infection of the eye that can be caused by a number of things, such as a blocked tear duct, a virus, bacteria, or allergies. It results in redness of the eye, itching, pain, and swelling. It is contagious, so it can spread into both eyes if it starts out in only one. Use the remedies below to treat this condition and treat both eyes at the same time, just in case.

Goldenrod eye wash and compress

Goldenrod (*Solidago odora*) is a common plant that appears in the fall months. Many people associate it with allergies, but goldenrod is not to blame for allergies. The likely allergy culprit that also blooms at the same time as goldenrod is ragweed. Goldenrod is a highly medicinal plant with strong antioxidant and anti–inflammatory properties. It makes a great eye wash for pink eye, for this reason. Here is how to make the eye wash.

Instructions:

1. Bring one cup of water to the boil on the stove.

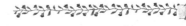

2. In a separate, sterile glass jar, add one tablespoon of goldenrod (aerial parts fresh or dried)

3. Carefully pour the water over the goldenrod.

4. Let this infuse for fifteen minutes with a lid on the jar.

5. Strain out the liquid through an unbleached coffee filter.

6. Wait for this to cool before washing your child's eyes with it.

7. Try to get it in the open eyes to wash out the infection properly.

8. Soak a clean cloth in the liquid.

9. Apply this to the eyes in between washings.

Chamomile eye wash and compress

Chamomile is antimicrobial and soothing. It can help reduce the redness and irritation brought on by pink eye, while also fighting the infection.

To make an eye wash:

1. Fill a jar with one tablespoon of chamomile flowers.

2. Pour a cup of boiling water over this.

3. Let it sit and infuse for fifteen minutes with a lid on.

4. Strain it out through an unbleached coffee filter.

5. When it is completely cooled, pour it over the eyes .

6. Try to get it in the open eyes to wash out the infection properly.

7. Soak a clean cloth in the liquid.

8. Apply this to the eyes in between washings.

The time between the ages of one and two can be a roller coaster ride in children's lives as they learn to walk, start to communicate better, and interact socially. With the ups, come the downs, such as dealing with the effects of viruses. However, with herbal remedies, you can be ready for whatever comes your way during this phase, as well as any other phase!

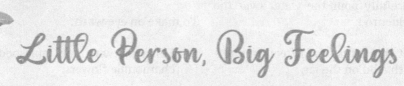

Little Person, Big Feelings

(Two to Three Years Old)

Magic happens in this phase between the ages of two and three –magic in the form of a powerful imagination! In this phase, your child may start playing make–believe and coming up with all kinds of fun characters and scenarios. Her mobility has really taken off at this point, and she should be kicking balls, running, jumping, and balancing. She will still have some way to go with the whole balance thing, though, so keep a close eye on her to prevent any accidents!

When it comes to emotions, you may notice your toddler showing a wider range of emotions and the desire to become more independent. This phase is often referred to as the "terrible twos," because there are a lot of emotions inside that your child doesn't yet know how to express properly . With all the physical, mental, and emotional activity, your child needs the proper amount of sleep each night, so it is important to make sure she is going to bed at a decent time and to allow naps during the day, if possible. In this chapter, you will learn how to help your little one get the sleep her body needs, as well as how to handle emotional issues like anxiety, using natural herbal remedies.

According to the Centers for Disease Control, your child needs at least eleven to fourteen hours of sleep each day, at the age of around two years (this includes daily naps). Sleep is vital at any age, as this is when our bodies recharge, grow, and regulate hormones. However, as they grow, young children often refuse to take a nap. If they aren't napping, they will likely be very ready for bed in the evening, but try to hold them off from falling asleep at 5pm, to prevent them from waking at 4am, bright-eyed and bushy-tailed. I learned this lesson the hard way. Not all toddlers get to sleep easily in the evening. If your child happens to be one who fights sleep and refuses to wind down before bedtime, there are a few steps you can take to help him:

1. **Avoid Blue Light:** Blue light, emitted through screens like computers, tablets, and cell phones, signals to our brains to stay awake and alert. This is why so many people are finding it hard to get to sleep, now more than ever. Staring at a blue light before bed is a surefire way to prevent restful sleep. Keep these devices away from your little one from at least three to four hours before bedtime.

2. **Establish a Bedtime Routine:** Routines are a beautiful thing and can help get your toddler into a sleepy mindset. A bedtime routine looks different for each family, but can consist of a pre-bedtime herbal bath (see recipe below), reading a book together in bed, saying prayers, doing bathroom stuff or picking out fun pajamas. Doing the same routine every night will eventually result in your toddler being ready for bedtime when it comes.

3. **Eliminate Loud Noises:** Do what you can to ensure your child isn't overstimulated by loud noises. Turn off the television and perhaps opt for turning on soft, gentle music. Classical music, turned down to a quiet volume, is an excellent choice.

4. **Turn Down the Lights:** Help signal to the brain that it's time for bed by turning down the lights about thirty minutes before going to bed. You don't have to walk around in darkness, but dimming the lights a bit is beneficial. Turn off all the bright lights in your home and keep a few lamps on.

5. **A Note on Melatonin:** While this supplement has gained popularity for getting a child to sleep, I highly encourage you to try other avenues before turning to melatonin. Even though it is sometimes marketed as "natural," it is not natural at all and is, in fact, made synthetically in a lab to simulate the actual melatonin hormone our pineal gland secretes as we go to sleep. The issue with melatonin supplements is that once you begin taking them, your pineal gland doesn't have to make its own any more, and gets accustomed to the supplement instead. If your child consistently takes these supplements, the pineal gland may

cease producing its own melatonin which will create a lifetime of dependency on the supplement. Try the natural remedies below, before turning to melatonin, to avoid putting your child's future sleep habits at risk.

Herbal Remedies for Sleep

In addition to the suggestions above, there are herbal remedies you can give, to help your child get a good night's sleep. Try one or more of the remedies below to help your child wind down and get ready for sleep.

Lavender Bath

Just the scent of lavender is enough to calm most people. Its lovely floral, yet herbaceous aroma is soothing and promotes feelings of peace and tranquility. You can help your little one wind down at bedtime by filling a muslin drawstring bag with three to four tablespoons of lavender buds and letting this sit in the bathtub as you run water and give your little one a pre-bedtime bath. Keep the curtain shut, as much as you can, to trap the aroma of the buds in the water while you wash your little one.

Chamomile Room Spray

Chamomile, like lavender, is another popular herb for soothing the mind and body to help bring on sleep. The scent is sweet and herbaceous and helps promote calm and rest. You can create a simple room spray to use before bed each night.

1. Boil three teaspoons of chamomile flowers in one cup of water until the liquid is reduced by half.

2. Then strain this out and blend it with one half cup of at least 80 proof alcohol (40% alcohol by volume).

3. Add this to a spray bottle and spray five to six times in your child's room.

4. There is no need to spray the bedding, just spray into the air in the room each night.

5. Because it is cut with alcohol, this preparation will have a longer shelf life than others.

6. It should be kept in the refrigerator, and will last for up to three months.

Catnip and Chamomile Tea

Catnip is famous for the crazy effect it has on our feline friends. However, it has exactly the opposite effect on humans! That's right – catnip is super calming to humans and can help us to wind down, chill out, and rest. It is a child-safe herb as well. When paired with chamomile , it can create a relaxing tea to promote restfulness and sleep for your toddler.

1. Infuse one teaspoon of each herb in a cup of hot water for ten to fifteen minutes.

2. Add a bit of raw honey to taste.

3. Let this cool to a drinkable temperature for your little one and allow her to sip on this, one hour before bed.

She doesn't need to drink the whole cup. Have her drink a small amount, around one half-cup or less. Refrigerate the rest for her to drink the following night. Too much, right before bed, can lead to bed-wetting, so make sure you give it one hour before bedtime so there is still a chance to use the restroom before turning in for the night.

Lavender Sachet

Another simple remedy you can utilize for your child is to fill a sachet with lavender buds and put this in your child's pillowcase – or better yet, inside a stuffed toy they sleep with. This keeps the calming scent of lavender with them throughout the night so they can rest peacefully. If the scent begins to fade (which doesn't happen quickly), you can add a couple of drops of essential oil to freshen it up. One of my favorite toys, while growing up, was a stuffed lamb with lavender rice inside. It could be heated up because of the rice and that also made the amazing smell of lavender waft across the room; it always helped me to sleep better.

Remedies for Anxiety and Emotional Distress

The two-to-three-year phase involves a lot of emotion as your child learns to navigate and express his feelings. There will likely be times when he has a hard time letting you know what he wants or how he feels, and this may result in a tantrum or anxiety. If you notice your child getting distressed, there are herbal remedies you can turn to that help calm and ground your child, and will help him feel better during these times.

Linden Blossom Calming Tea

Linden blossoms are sweet-smelling flowers that have been used for centuries to curb anxiety, especially in children. They are one of the best child-safe remedies to promote calm and peace. My grandmother always kept a stock of the lovely blossoms because they worked so well for her own children, and then for her grandkids too. Create a soothing tea for your child to enjoy during times of frustration by following the instructions.

1. Infuse one to two teaspoons of linden blossom in one cup of hot water for ten to fifteen minutes.

2. Add raw honey to taste and give this to your child as needed.

3. Another great way to utilize this tea is to freeze it into popsicles for your child to enjoy.

Lemon Balm Nervine Candy

Lemon balm is a gentle and effective nervine that can help to soothe frustration and frazzled nerves. An additional benefit of lemon balm is its antiviral properties, so it is a great herb to have around for those reasons! Use the herb fresh, when possible, to maximize the antiviral benefits. This member of the mint family is also one of the tastiest of the mints, with an invigorating, lemony flavor and refreshing scent. It is perfect for making into a candy for your little one to enjoy, if he is struggling with anxiety.

Ingredients:

* Lemon balm, water, and raw honey

Instructions:

1. Have parchment paper spread out and ready for this process beforehand.

2. Boil one cup of water with three tablespoons of lemon balm for fifteen minutes.

3. Once it has cooled a bit, strain out the liquid.

4. Add the strained liquid back into the pot.

5. Add one cup of raw honey and blend it on low to medium heat.

6. Let this come to a gentle boil and have a candy thermometer handy.

7. Keep taking the temperature and stirring the syrup.

8. When the temperature reaches 300°F (150°C), you are ready to drop the mixture onto parchment paper.

9. Scoop small volumes of syrup into a spoon and carefully drop little drops onto the parchment paper. Try to keep the drops nickel- to quarter-sized.

10. They will begin to harden and turn into candy as they cool.

11. Dust your candies with powdered cinnamon or ginger to keep them from sticking to each other when you put them in a jar for storage.

12. Don't place them in the jar until they are completely cooled and hardened, and dusted with cinnamon or ginger powder.

13. They will last in the refrigerator for at least six months.

14. Take one as needed, for anxiety and stress.

15. Be sure to keep an eye on your child when giving this candy so she doesn't choke.

Lavender & Catnip Popsicles

Lavender is one of the most famous plants for helping to calm and soothe. It is extremely effective and one of the safest herbs for children. And catnip isn't just awesome for helping a little one wind down in order to sleep soundly; it can also be used to help calm anxiety. When these two are combined, they create a doubly calming herbal remedy that tastes wonderful, even to the sensitive palate of a child! Follow the instructions to make a tasty popsicle.

1. Create a tea with one or two teaspoons each of lavender and catnip infused into a cup of hot water for fifteen to twenty minutes.

2. Add raw honey to taste and blend this well.

3. You can choose to pour this into popsicle molds as is, or blend it with some of your child's favorite juice and then pour into molds.

4. Give one to your child during times when she seems frustrated or overwhelmed.

5. They can also be enjoyed an hour or two before bed, if your child has trouble winding down.

It is normal for children to have tantrums and emotional outbursts during this phase of childhood. They are learning how to deal with everything and sometimes all those feelings inside can be a bit too much for them to express. As a parent, being able to look past what you see on the surface and understand that your child is experiencing real feelings that she hasn't yet learned how to control, is key. Empathize with her, from her perspective, instead of downplaying her feelings, ignoring them, or shaming them. Use the remedies outlined above as needed. As children mature, these "tantrums" will likely disappear, but they will know that you are there for them through every issue they encounter, as you have been from the beginning.

Potty Training

This is also an exciting time as your child may be showing signs of readiness to be potty trained! Some signs you will want to look for are:

• Your child shows an interest in going to the potty.

• Your child understands and can verbalize about using the potty. For example, when he tells you he pooped or peed in his diaper.

• Your child can make the connection between the need to use the potty and the act of doing so.

• He can follow directions and try to imitate you.

- Your child can get on and off the potty and stay seated long enough to do what is necessary.

- Your child can take off his diaper, or pull his pants up or down by himself.

If your child is showing signs of readiness, there are ways you can make training easier.

- Introduce the training potty early so your child gets used to it and isn't afraid.

- Put the training potty in a place that is convenient for your child.

- Get your child on a potty schedule. For example, take her to the bathroom to try using the potty every hour or two.

- Use a sticker chart to track her progress and make it fun for her to learn. Let her help pick out the chart for even more personalization.

- Use rewards when she succeeds in using the potty. These can be small candies (especially herbal ones like the recipe above), toys, a sticker they can stick somewhere interesting.

- Find or create a potty song you can sing together.

- Shower her with praise anytime she tries to use the potty, and especially when she succeeds.

- Give your child a book to read while on the potty, to help her sit for long enough.

Nighttime training usually takes longer than daytime training, but don't worry. It will all happen in good time. You and your child may need to take a break sometimes; that's ok! Just pick up where you left off when you're both ready. There's no need to make it any more stressful than it has to be. Some children take longer; in fact, boys often take longer than girls, but, again, it is absolutely okay. If you are concerned though, talk to your pediatrician.

But, Teddy Bear Loves Me ...

(Three to Four Years Old)

By three years of age, most children have a full set of primary teeth, so make sure they are taking care of those pearly whites! Additionally, a child of this age is beginning to put what he knows to the test by applying the concepts he learns. This is the age at which many children are sent to preschool. Teachers expect children to be able to identify some shapes, colors, and numbers, as well as to communicate in longer, more complex sentences. Children in this phase understand more complex commands as well, and can often carry out three-part commands like, "Pick up your blocks, put them in the box, and turn off the light when you are done playing in that room."

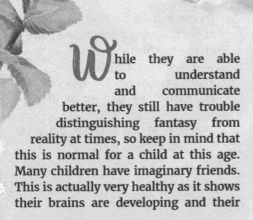

While they are able to understand and communicate better, they still have trouble distinguishing fantasy from reality at times, so keep in mind that this is normal for a child at this age. Many children have imaginary friends. This is actually very healthy as it shows their brains are developing and their imaginations are in full swing. More introverted children may keep their imaginary friends for longer than other children. This too is perfectly normal. I actually had my imaginary friend, Sara, until late in childhood. I still remember her well; she looked like me, but could fly.

Each child develops differently, and

some may not quite be ready to listen to lengthy commands. Paying close attention is not a strong point at this phase, but allowing your child time to mature at her own pace will likely save you a lot of worry and frustration. In this chapter, you will learn how to make your own natural toothpaste to nourish your child's teeth, as well as herbal remedies for issues like Attention Deficit Hyperactivity Disorder (ADHD), and common health issues like allergies.

Teeth are indicative of our overall health in some ways. Proper dental care, like brushing your teeth at least twice daily, can keep mouth bacteria at bay. When the body doesn't have to fight these bacteria, it takes a strain off the immune system so it can fight other pathogens more efficiently. From the time your baby is born, you can practice good oral care by brushing the emerging teeth with a gentle finger brush and a pea-sized drop of fluoride-free toothpaste. By the time they are three to four years old, children should understand the concept of spitting out toothpaste when they brush their teeth. Now you can create your own, natural toothpaste at home that helps to kill bacteria in the mouth so your child's immune system can function optimally.

Natural Toothpaste Recipe

This recipe helps kill bacteria in the mouth using ground cloves and peppermint. Other simple and common ingredients blend with these herbs to create an effective and safe toothpaste for the whole family:

Ingredients:

- ½ cup coconut oil
- 2-3 TBSP baking soda
- 2 small packets stevia (*Stevia rebaudiana*) powder
- 2 tsp powdered cloves
- 2 tsp powdered peppermint leaves

Instructions:

1. Melt the coconut oil by sitting the container in a pan of warm water until enough is melted to get half a cup.

2. Pour the half cup of coconut oil into a medium-sized mixing bowl.

3. Add the baking soda, stevia, cloves, and peppermint leaves and blend everything together thoroughly.

4. Let this sit and cool, giving it a stir, occasionally, to keep everything distributed evenly in the coconut oil as it hardens.

5. Before it completely hardens, put the preparation in a sterile glass jar for safekeeping.

6. To use it, take a small amount out of the jar using a spoon and place it on the toothbrush.

7. Brush your teeth for two minutes and then rinse out your mouth.

8. Use this at least twice daily for best results.

Coconut Oil Pulling for Oral Health

Coconut oil contains a compound called lauric acid which is known for its antimicrobial properties. This is one reason why it is so popular for oil pulling. What is oil pulling? It is simply the process of swishing coconut oil in your mouth for several minutes so it can "pull" out bad bacteria and microorganisms. When you practice this daily, you can reduce your chances of developing gingivitis, plaque, and bad bacteria in the mouth. Oil pulling with coconut oil is perfect for those who wish to go the extra mile to prevent tooth decay and other oral issues. If you think your child is capable of swishing a little coconut oil in her mouth for one minute, give it a try! She will need to be able to spit it out when she has finished swishing, because the coconut oil will be full of bacteria and undesirable organisms that shouldn't be swallowed.

Have your child take a small amount of coconut oil, around one teaspoon, and swish it in her mouth. It will melt quite fast in the mouth and become liquid. If she is able to do this for one minute, that is optimal, but if she cannot, try working your way up to a minute over the course of several weeks of practice. The whole family can take advantage of oil pulling for healthy teeth and gums.

Remedies for ADHD

As mentioned at the beginning of this chapter, your child may start understanding you better at this stage in his development. However, this doesn't mean all children will be following through with three-step commands and paying close attention

to your every word. It is simply not realistic to expect children to all follow the same developmental curve at the same pace. When my oldest son was two years old, we went in for our yearly pediatric health-check. My son was in an unfamiliar place (we didn't go to the pediatrician that often) and there were toys and books everywhere for him to play with. The doctor came into the room and was trying to talk to him, but my son was busy playing with all the new toys and taking in all the new sights. He didn't make much eye contact with the doctor, as a result.

I was shocked when the doctor turned to me and said, "He isn't making much eye contact when I talk to him and he seems a bit hyperactive." I just stared at him, speechless. He then suggested we put my two-year-old son on medication for ADHD. I was appalled. As his mom, I knew he made eye contact all the time with us and I also knew him well enough at that point to know that he was in a new place with all kinds of new toys to distract him from the boring doctor. I wasn't about to put my toddler on medication to sedate him. We ended up leaving that doctor, shortly after the encounter. I will never forget how willing he was to put my little one on medication after a very brief, two-minute encounter with him.

My son is now eleven years old and at the top of his class. He has a high school reading level and is a sweet, kind, boy who is not hyperactive at all. I am so glad I listened to my motherly instincts instead of blindly listening to that doctor! Because of variations in normal childhood activity levels, most doctors are hesitant to diagnose something like ADHD until a child is at least five years old.

But there were times when I questioned whether or not my son had issues with hyperactivity. He was into everything, curious, destructive at times, and bounced from one thing to another. My feelings quickly changed when I started arranging playdates with other moms and their young sons. Watching the other boys play, I realized that my son was just like the other boys, and his behavior was that of a normal little boy! Society, and some medical professionals, tries to fit children into a box of what is considered "normal." If they don't fit into that box, they are sometimes labeled as "different," "hyperactive," or "overly emotional." Society's remedy is to medicate most of these children.

While I believe there are some children who may need medication, I also believe that many children are being medicated when they absolutely do not need it. A doctor attempted to put my son in a box and I refused. The overly curious nature that bothered my doctor now benefits my son, as he has won numerous science awards for his experiments. These behaviors in our children, that some see as negative, can most certainly be molded into something positive down the road. Additionally, there are plenty of herbal remedies you can utilize to help your child calm down and become more grounded if you are concerned about his behavior. And unlike the prescription medications, these natural remedies come without the harmful side effects.

Grounding Room Spray

Vetiver (*Chrysopogon zizanioides*) has a rich, grounding effect. It is often used to help one take pause and find mental and emotional support. You can create a safe, non-toxic grounding spray to use around your child when she needs support. It can be sprayed in a fine mist on clothing, and won't stain most materials (test a spot first). You can also spray a light misting in her room to help her calm down, or wherever you are when you notice her struggling. The aroma of vetiver root is relaxing, comforting, and quieting for both children and adults.

Ingredients:

• One cup of water

• One tablespoon of chopped vetiver root

Instructions:

1. Bring water to the boil then add vetiver root.

2. Reduce heat to a simmer and let the mixture simmer for ten minutes.

3. Remove from heat and allow the infusion to cool.

4. Strain it and bottle it in a spray bottle.

5. To prolong the shelf life, you can cut it with an equal amount of grain alcohol. This will extend its shelf life to around six months, if stored in the refrigerator.

Rosemary Focus Oil

William Shakespeare said it best in his play, *Hamlet*: "Rosemary for remembrance." Even in the Middle Ages, rosemary (*Salvia rosmarinus*) had a reputation for helping with memory and focus. Rosemary is a common garden herb that is easily grown in most regions. You can follow the oil infusion protocol in <u>harnessing the essence of herbs chapter</u> to create a rosemary oil to help your child with focus and grounding. An oil infusion is much safer than an essential oil, especially when it comes to rosemary. Rosemary is completely safe when used with children in an oil infusion, but the *essential oil* is highly concentrated and contains high levels of a compound called 1,8-cineole (or eucalyptol) that can potentially be harmful to children under the age of ten. You can rest assured that using the herb infusion is completely safe, as it is not as concentrated. Apply a small amount of this oil to the back of the ears, neck, and wrists as needed, for focus and grounding. It helps to store it in a roller bottle to make application easier (this works for any carrier oil except unfractionated coconut oil).

Remedies for Allergies

In the spring and fall months you may notice that your child has a runny nose and red, watery eyes. If this is the case, there are plenty of herbal remedies you can employ to help control the release of histamine and keep your child comfortable. In addition to the remedies below, consider booking an appointment with your local chiropractor for an adjustment to keep your child's ears draining correctly and prevent ear infections.

Purple Deadnettle Tea: Allergy Relief in your Backyard

Purple deadnettle (*Lamium purpureum*) is a member of the mint family, although it doesn't taste minty at all. It is one of the most common yard "weeds" that pops up in early spring and stays around throughout the summer months. It is a small, unassuming plant that one might easily overlook if not paying attention. It has a square stem and tiny pink flowers at the top. The toothed leaves turn a purple tint near the top of the plant. Picture of plant It is often confused with another, similar plant called henbit, although they are two different species with different properties . Purple deadnettle contains flavonoids that help to suppress histamine production. This makes it an excellent and readily available choice for allergy relief.

1. Infuse two teaspoons of fresh, or one teaspoon of dried, aerial parts into one cup of hot water for fifteen minutes.

2. Have your child drink around one half cup per day (you can space this out into multiple small doses if you want).

3. Add raw honey for a more pleasant taste.

Stinging Nettle Allergy Tea

Stinging nettle sounds formidable, but it is a plant full of medicinal potential when used correctly. True, it must be handled with gloves because it has tiny, stinging hairs that can cause skin irritation. However, once the leaves are cooked or steamed, the hairs are no trouble. This valuable plant is a great source of numerous vitamins, minerals, and flavonoids, making it a favorite among herbalists for supporting overall health. Like purple deadnettle, it contains flavonoids that help to suppress histamine production.

1. Infuse two teaspoons of the dried and chopped nettle leaves into one cup of hot water for fifteen minutes to make an allergy tea.

2. Children can drink one half cup at intervals throughout the day for allergy relief.

3. Add raw honey to improve taste.

Elderberry Candies for Allergies

Elderberry is known for its antiviral and immunomodulatory properties, but it is also a great allergy tamer because of its quercetin content. Quercetin helps relieve allergies by lowering inflammation in the airways and promoting healthy breathing. For those who suffer with allergies, quercetin-rich foods and plants like elderberry can reduce the occurrence of coughs, watery eyes, runny noses, hives, swollen lips or tongue, and other allergy-related symptoms. You can give your child elderberry glycerite from the previous chapter, for allergies (give five milliliters daily during allergy season), or you can make easy-to-take candies with elderberry.

Instructions:

1. In a pot, cover elderberries with water that reaches one inch (2.5 cm) above the berries. Bring this to a boil.

2. Let this simmer, covered, for one hour.

3. Strain out the juice from this and return it to the pan.

4. Add an equal amount of honey to the juice and blend this together well.

5. Let this come to a boil and keep an eye on the temperature using a candy thermometer.

6. Allow this to reach 300°F (150°C) and then use a spoon to drop small amounts of the syrup onto parchment paper in nickel- to quarter-sized drops.

7. Allow these to cool and coat them in powdered ginger or cinnamon to keep them from sticking together when you place them in a sterile glass container for storage.

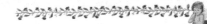

8. Keep the candies in the refrigerator and give them to your child, three to four daily, during allergy season, to tame allergies.

9. These candies should be kept in the refrigerator for no longer than six months.

Pine for Respiratory Health

Pine and fir (*Abies*) trees produce needles that are wonderfully child-safe for supporting respiratory health. The best part is that they are available year-round to use as you need them! You can harvest enough to fill a jar and make an oil infusion to rub on your child's chest. This helps to open up airways and relieve congestion. Try this before bedtime to ensure your little one gets a good night's sleep, as well as some much-needed relief from allergy symptoms.

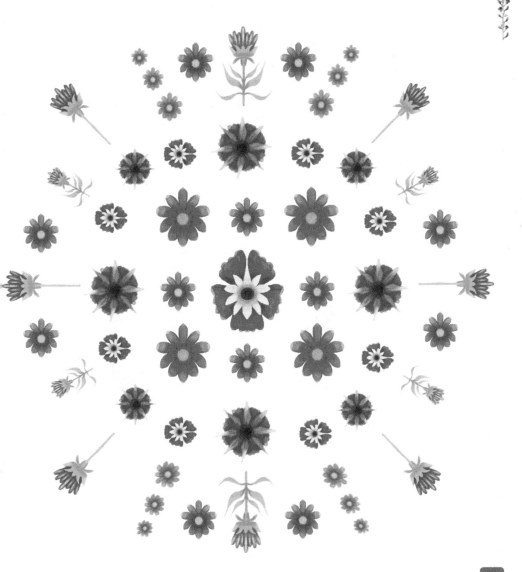

Sneaky Little Bugs

(Four to Five Years Old)

This phase of childhood involves many tears, both happy and sad. It is a time of great milestones, firsts, and lessons learned for both child and parents! Some parents will be sending their little ones off to kindergarten at the end of this phase, or enrolling them in preschool for the first time. Watching your little one walk into her classroom on the first day of school can be both heartbreaking and heartwarming for a parent. This is also a time when children can pick up bugs from other children at school. "Bugs" can come in different forms … First, there are the annoying gastrointestinal viruses that cause stomach and digestive upsets. Not to worry, there are herbal remedies you can employ to help your child feel better fast! Then there are also actual bugs, like lice. These can be dealt with naturally as well, and you don't have to worry about treating your child's tender scalp with toxic substances. In this chapter, you will learn how to combat various gastrointestinal issues like an upset stomach, nausea, diarrhea, and constipation, as well as how to deal with head lice using natural remedies.

"My Tummy Hurts"

The phrase above strikes fear into the hearts of many parents. What is my child going to do next? Is he going to throw up everywhere? Is he sick? What if it is his appendix? If your child complains of an upset stomach, monitor him closely. Have him take it easy and lie down. Take his temperature to see if he has a fever. Keep him hydrated. This is worth repeating: keep him hydrated! Push water as often as possible, so he is properly hydrated should he vomit or come down with something. Have your herbal popsicles ready to go, just in case. Have him lie on his side if his stomach hurts and consider applying a warm compress like a heat pad. This can help dispel gas that may be causing pain.

The question of whether or not the stomach pain is due to an appendix can be addressed by asking your child where the pain is coming from. Appendix pain often comes on suddenly and is located in the lower right side of the abdomen. It can begin around the navel area and then shift to the lower right side. If the pain worsens when the child coughs, jumps, or makes other jarring movements, it may be a sign that something is amiss with the appendix. Other things to look for include nausea, vomiting, and a loss of appetite. If you do suspect the appendix, take your child to the hospital as soon as possible. If you suspect your child has a stomach bug or another gastrointestinal issue, try one of the remedies below.

Peppermint and Chamomile Tea for Upset Stomach

Both peppermint and chamomile are excellent carminative herbs, meaning they help soothe stomach and digestive woes. Peppermint is wonderfully invigorating and soothing to an upset stomach, and chamomile can help quieten spasms and quell gas pains.

Instructions:

1. Combine one teaspoon of each herb to infuse in one cup of hot water for ten to fifteen minutes to make a tea for tummy aches.

2. Add raw honey to taste and allow this to cool sufficiently before allowing your child a drink.

3. If your child doesn't like warm beverages, you may pour the tea into popsicle molds and let her enjoy it in this form instead.

Ginger and Spearmint for Nausea

Just the scent of ginger and spearmint can eliminate feelings of nausea for many people. If your child is complaining of being sick to the stomach, try letting her inhale the aroma of one teaspoon of chopped ginger root and one teaspoon of crushed spearmint leaves, blended in a jar. She can just sit there with it and inhale as needed. Alternatively, make a tea as described below.

Instructions:

1. Infuse one teaspoon of crushed spearmint leaves and one teaspoon of chopped ginger root into one cup of hot water for ten minutes.

2. Allow your child to drink this if she can. Sometimes it can be hard to get a child who is nauseous to drink anything.

3. Again, if you are having trouble, add some raw honey to the tea and pour it into a popsicle mold to let her enjoy its benefits.

Agrimony Tea for Diarrhea

Diarrhea is not something to ignore in children. Their little bodies lose so much water that it is imperative to keep them hydrated to compensate for this water loss. Try pushing water, along with herbal popsicles, as much as possible. Agrimony (*Agrimonia eupatoria*) is a soothing and child-friendly herb that can help soothe an upset stomach and gastrointestinal tract, helping your child recover from diarrhea faster.

Instructions:

1. Make a tea with agrimony roots and aerial parts by infusing one to two teaspoons of agrimony into one cup

of hot water for fifteen minutes.

2. Add raw honey to taste and have your child drink this.

3. Encourage your child to finish the cup by the time she goes to bed. She can drink small amounts throughout the day, if needed.

Activated Charcoal for Diarrhea and Vomiting

In addition to agrimony tea, activated charcoal capsules can work wonders for those with a gastrointestinal virus that causes diarrhea and vomiting. Activated charcoal helps flush out toxins and pathogens that cause damage in the body. It draws them out and helps rid the body of these unwanted germs. Even today, some emergency room doctors use this to treat overdoses and poisonings because it successfully brings the toxins out of the body. Even though it flushes out toxins, activated charcoal is NOT a diuretic, making it safe for those with diarrhea and vomiting. This substance is available in many forms, so you can purchase the form that is easiest for your child to take. Follow the directions on the bottle.

Prune Juice for Constipation

Constipation is an all-too common trend among young children. This is largely due to a diet poor in fiber. To avoid constipation, try to make sure your little one is getting enough fiber each day and eating a variety of different foods, especially vegetables and fruits. Avoid processed foods and too much meat. In addition, avoid excessive amounts of cheese or other dairy, as this is very binding. One of my kids had to adopt a dairy-free diet for a few years because, no matter how small the amount she ate, it would constipate her. We substituted almond milk. If your child is constipated, keep her hydrated and push water over other forms of hydration. If you find that your child is still having issues with constipation, have her drink a little organic prune juice each day. For a child between the ages of four and five, try giving four ounces (120 ml) of prune juice daily. If the child has trouble drinking all of this at once, space it out in two equal doses per day instead. If you notice the child becoming more regular, you can taper this down to one two-ounce (60 ml) serving daily, for maintenance. Dried prunes can also be eaten in lieu of the juice if your child prefers.

Organic Apple Juice for Constipation Maintenance

For mild constipation, try using organic apple juice instead of prune juice. Prune juice can be stronger than apple juice and may be too strong for mild cases of constipation. And some children simply don't like the taste of prune juice. Let your child have one glass of organic apple juice daily if he struggles with regular bowel movements. Then, if you still don't see an improvement after several weeks, you can start using prune juice.

Lice: Don't Freak Out

Let me tell you a short story from my childhood that still haunts my nightmares to this day. I was in second grade and rode the bus home from school every day. (The school bus is the perfect place for a child to get head lice because there are a lot of children sitting close together in a small space.) One day I got home from school with not a care in the world and was excited to see my mom and dad. My mom greeted me at the door and all was well ... until she noticed me scratch my head. (A little about my mom: she prefers everything to be very neat and hates bugs of all kinds.) You can imagine her reaction when she took a pencil and started moving it around my scalp to part my hair, and found head lice everywhere! Head lice and eggs!

She lost it. She was sobbing, screaming, and running through the house like a madwoman. I was just a little seven-year-old girl and relied on my mom to know that everything was okay. So when she freaked out, I freaked out. She spent the next ten hours picking through my hair with a fine-tooth comb while sobbing, bagging up toys, burning things, and vacuuming like her life depended on it. She put common, over-the-counter head lice treatment on my head and let it sit for who knows how long. She treated herself and every family member, whether they needed it or not. I ended up having chemical burns on my scalp from the harsh chemicals in the head lice treatment.

Needless to say, I was traumatized. It wasn't the head lice that traumatized me – it was my mom's reaction to them. If I can relate one thing to the reader, it is this: please try to stay calm in the face of whatever comes at you or your children. Your reaction goes a long way in assuring your child that everything will be okay and that the world is not in fact burning to the ground. Below are some head lice remedies that help to suffocate the lice without the harsh chemicals that can cause serious scalp dermatitis.

Oil Hair Mask

To successfully suffocate head lice, you need to have a good amount of thick oil on hand. Two great oils for this job are coconut oil and olive oil. Those are two pretty common cooking oils, so one of them is probably in your kitchen right now! Before slathering on the oil, use a fine-tooth comb to go through your child's hair and pick out as many lice and lice eggs as possible. The tiny, white eggs are attached to the strands of hair. It takes a good comb to remove them. Once you feel like you have removed everything you see, you can slather on a liberal amount of either olive or coconut oil. Don't leave any hair uncovered. Put it on as thickly as you can.

Once the head and hair are completely covered in oil, place a shower cap on and hang out. Be patient. Leave it on as long as you can. Sleep in it, if possible. The best thing about this treatment is that it won't harm your hair (I can't say the same for the over-the-counter treatment used on my hair when I was a child). If anything, these oils help to hydrate and moisturize the hair so it is even healthier afterwards. After at least twelve hours, wash the oil out and shampoo your hair like you normally would. Go back over the scalp and pick out any eggs you may have missed. Blow dry your hair. This helps to kill any leftover lice. Repeat this until the lice are all gone. They are usually taken care of after one treatment, but if you are still concerned, it never hurts to do it again.

Bag it Up

Depending on how long your child has had the lice, you will likely need to take a few extra steps to make sure there are none in your home. Bag up all your child's stuffed toys and place them in an airtight trash bag for a few weeks or put them in the dryer on high temperature for as long as you can. Wash all bedding in the house. Put the hair accessories that your family has used in a freezer bag and leave it in the freezer overnight. Rather than go through your house cleaning in a frenzy, take into consideration that lice cannot live for more than two days without a meal, so they tend to stick around where they can get an easy meal. These will be areas where your child has been in the last two days. Check these specific places and feel free to vacuum there, spread baking soda, salt, or diatomaceous earth (these natural substances kill lice and other pests like fleas), and then vacuum again. Wear a mask if you use diatomaceous earth. It is completely natural, but shouldn't be inhaled into the lungs. Check your child's backpack when she comes home from school, as this is usually in close proximity to her head. Wash all hats, coats, and clothing that your child has worn in the past two days.

Remember that, as the parent, you set the tone for your child's day. You have a big impact on how she perceives the world around her, and you can encourage her to perceive things from a positive or a negative perspective. Having a positive attitude can be hard when your child is sick and you are scared, but with the herbal remedies for stomach issues, you have some control over the situation. The same goes with lice. This too shall pass!

Other Parasites

Other parasites, ones that aren't as easily seen, are intestinal parasites. Children often pick these up by eating or drinking contaminated food, non-food items (feces, either human or animal), or water. According to the CDC (CDC, 2020), infants, toddlers, and young children in daycares are particularly at risk of contracting a parasite disease called giardiasis that causes diarrhea and is spread through contaminated feces. Pinworm infection (enterobiasis), the most common intestinal parasite, also happens most often among preschool and young school-age children.

Soil-transmitted helminth diseases ("helminth" means parasitic worm) are caused by infection with roundworm, hookworm or whipworm, and can include symptoms of diarrhea, abdominal pain, intestinal obstruction, anemia, and stunted growth, as well as impaired cognitive development. Infection occurs by ingesting roundworm and whipworm eggs that have matured in soil contaminated by human feces, or by walking barefoot in contaminated soil where human hookworm eggs have hatched. These infections aren't as common in developed countries as they are in developing countries, but still happen sometimes. Symptoms, and their severity, can vary, as does treatment protocol. Seeking a doctor's help is best.

Parasites can spread very quickly so don't wait to seek medical help if you suspect your child has an intestinal parasite. The best prevention for intestinal parasites is washing hands thoroughly, including under fingernails. It is also important to teach children not to not scratch their bare bottoms, suck on their fingers, or eat/drink anything they shouldn't.

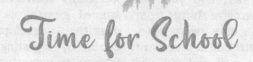

Time for School

(Five to Ten Years Old)

They grow up so fast! This phase tends to fly by, trust me. One minute you are waving goodbye to your little kindergartner and the next day you are helping her prepare for middle school. Treasure each and every moment! In this phase of development, you get to see your child grow into a more mature young person. When I say "mature," I mean your child will start looking out for the feelings of others and becoming more empathetic. Children of this age realize that they aren't the center of the world and others have feelings too. In this phase, my oldest son started becoming more aware of this and began sticking up for his friends and himself more. This was the phase where he stopped playing with most of his "kid" toys and started playing with STEM projects and Legos. I still get teary-eyed when I think about how he used to love certain toys and those days are now long gone.

Children in this age group may experience growing pains as their bodies grow. This is completely normal, but can be painful. Speaking of pain, they may experience other types of pain too. In this chapter, you will learn how you can identify and tackle growing pains, as well as other types of physical pain like bumps, bruises, and sprains.

What are Growing Pains?

One night my son woke us up, crying and saying his legs hurt. We were at a loss as to what the problem could be. He was obviously in pain and I wanted to help, but I had no idea what could be causing leg pain in an eight-year-old boy. Later, I learned that he had "growing pains." Growing pains are characterized by pain in the legs, specifically the front of the thighs, the calves or behind the knees. This pain often feels like an ache or throbbing in the areas mentioned. Growing pains are very common between the ages of five and ten. The joints of the legs look normal when a child is experiencing growing pains. There is no redness and no swollen areas are visible. I ended up taking my son to the hospital because we had no idea what was causing his pain. Of course, we learned that there was nothing wrong with him and that he was perfectly healthy. Since having more children, we now know what growing pains are, as well as how to treat them naturally. Below are some effective remedies for growing pains.

Magnesium Sulfate Soak and Heat Packs

If your child is experiencing growing pains, one of the best ways to provide comfort and help him feel better fast is to run him a warm bath and add one or two cups of Epsom salts. Epsom salts contain magnesium sulfate which can help to soothe sore muscles and reduce pain. This, coupled with soaking in warm water, can work wonders for growing pains when they occur. Try using rice heat packs on the affected areas as well, to reduce pain if a bath is not an option. You can also add herbs such as lavender, peppermint, or rosemary to help soothe. You can put them in a muslin bag to make cleaning up easier.

Vitamin D

Vitamin D is essential to healthy bones, but that's not all. This vitamin plays an important role in other bodily functions, such as cell growth, neuromuscular and immune function, and glucose metabolism. Most people are deficient in this vitamin, especially in the winter months when the sun shines less. The best way to get this vitamin is for your body to absorb sunlight through the skin, and use it to manufacture the vitamin. A little time in the sun goes a long way to promoting healthy bones, joints, and a healthy immune system. Let your child spend time outdoors, as much as possible. It is recommended that everyone spend around twenty minutes in the sun daily, without sunscreen, for optimal vitamin D production.

If time in the sun isn't an option, you can always take a vitamin D supplement that contains the different essential variants (e.g., D2, D3). Supplements will not absorb into the body as easily as vitamin D made via natural routes like sunlight, but they can still be handy for helping keep the levels where they need to be.

Pain Control

Before you reach for the over-the-counter pain relievers, there are natural remedies that target inflammation and pain as well. And these remedies seek to tackle the root of the pain instead of just masking a larger issue. Below are more remedies for different types of pain your child may encounter as she grows.

Tooth Pain

There are many reasons your child could have tooth pain, but it is always best to first see a dentist to address the issue. This helps rule out any potentially dangerous issues, like an infection. Once you know what you are dealing with, you can better treat the issue at hand. For mouth pain, try one of the remedies below.

Toothache Plant Tincture

If you need something to treat pain in the mouth fast, you can use the toothache plant (*Acmella oleracea*). It is a petalless flower that happens to have the unique ability to completely numb the area where it is applied. It is nature's lidocaine. Toothache plant is easy to grow in most climates and the flowering tops can be harvested and tinctured to create a potent and pain-numbing remedy. (Harnessing the essence of herbs) You need only apply one or two drops of this tincture to the affected area to see results. Like lidocaine, the toothache plant may cause excess drooling as your mouth numbs. Apply this every few hours as needed for tooth pain. You can also grab a leaf or flower head straight off the plant and chew it.

Clove Oil for Tooth Pain

Clove is gentler than the toothache plant, when it comes to numbing ability, but it is a very effective pain reliever for mouth pain. You can make an oil infusion with cloves by using olive oil (or any other oil that is safe for ingestion). Apply a small amount of this oil to the affected area as needed for pain.

Yarrow

Yarrow is also an effective anesthetic. You can make a poultice with the root and leaves, and apply directly to the area, or you can make it into a tincture or infused oil, or even chew the leaves fresh off the plant.

Sprains, Contusions, and Inflammation

I had never had a sprain until I was well into adulthood, and hope your child never has to deal with one! However, life with kids is full of bumps and bruises, so if they do have an accident you can be ready with remedies to help control the pain, inflammation, and bruising that come with sprained ankles and wrists.

Comfrey Leaf Wrap for Inflammation and Pain

Comfrey has been used for centuries for helping to reduce inflammation and pain when it comes to swelling and contusions of all kinds. It is safer to apply topically, and the leaves can be placed right on the affected area and covered in plastic wrap to hold them in place. You can leave this on the area for several hours and then remove it and replace it with another leaf, as needed, until the swelling subsides. *Avoid applying leaves to broken skin as this can cause irritation and risk infection.*

Cabbage Leaf Wrap

If you don't have comfrey leaves available, cabbage (*Brassica oleracea*) leaves are another surprisingly excellent anti-inflammatory to treat contusions and sprains. Like comfrey, the leaves can be applied directly to the affected area and left on for several hours. When they appear wilted, you can remove them and apply fresh ones. Cover the area in plastic wrap to hold the leaves in place. Both comfrey and cabbage leaves help reduce inflammation caused by trauma in the area. When the inflammation is reduced, the pain is often reduced as well.

Cabbage leaves are also best used after being heated in hot water till the leaves are a bright green.This means the enzymes in the plant are at their best. As soon as they have gone pale or translucent you have heated them too much and they don't work as well. Apply the leaves in the same manner as above, but make sure the leaves are not too hot for your skin.

Arnica Oil for Bruises

For bruises and bumps, arnica is among the top herbs for relieving the swelling and pain, while also promoting healing of tissues in the area. Arnica is especially great for pain relief, and is often used in various commercial and homemade pain remedies, both herbal and homeopathic. Arnica flowers can be infused into a skin-nourishing carrier oil using the oil infusion protocol to create an oil you can apply to all kinds of contusions. This oil can make your child feel better in no time, but always keep in mind that it should never be applied to broken skin. Arnica is perfectly safe when applied topically to unbroken skin, but if it gets into the bloodstream through wounds, it can be toxic. Use in diluted doses for maximum safety and be very careful with this.

Ginger Oil for Pain relief

Ginger is known for its anti-inflammatory and analgesic (pain-relieving) properties, so it is no wonder it makes a very effective topical remedy for swollen and painful areas resulting from trauma. One of the easiest ways to make a topical salve with ginger is to use ground ginger. It absorbs into the oil well. Use the beeswax and oil protocol to make a salve with powdered ginger (Page 23). Add two teaspoons of powdered ginger to the double boiler when creating this salve. This can be safely applied to children of any age when they experience painful bumps and bruises.

For adults needing a remedy for painful joints, you can create this salve and add two teaspoons of ground cayenne powder, along with the two teaspoons of ground ginger powder, to create an effective topical remedy for arthritis and other inflammatory conditions.

Headaches

A headache can be caused by many triggers, ranging from screen time to the weather. If your child is complaining of a headache, try not to fret too much. If headaches become a recurring problem, you should make an appointment to see your doctor for more insight. For the occasional headache, there are herbal remedies you can try to help provide relief and respite.

Peppermint Headache Compress (Hot or Cold)

Peppermint leaves aren't just great for opening up the respiratory tract and helping soothe an upset stomach. They are naturally analgesic and can help relieve headaches. One of the best ways to use peppermint for a headache is described below.

1. Create a tea with the leaves by infusing two or three teaspoons of the leaves into one cup of hot water for fifteen to twenty minutes.

2. Allow the tea to cool.

3. Soak a clean cloth into the tea and wring it out well.

4. Apply this to the head, back of neck, or face.

5. Allow this to sit on the area for as long as possible.

6. For added relief, you can allow the tea to cool to the point where it is warm but not hot, and apply this warm compress to the face.

7. For some people, a cold compress helps get rid of headaches better, so if this is the case for your child, let the tea cool completely by placing it in the refrigerator before soaking the cloth.

Chamomile Headache Tea

Chamomile is a flower with many attributes, and pain relief is definitely one! Chamomile is perfect for headaches triggered by tension. This nervine flower can help relieve pain by releasing tension that may be contributing to the headache. Additionally, it can help calm the body and mind to promote relaxation and peace so your child can feel better faster. The scent alone can help calm headaches for some people.

1. Infuse two teaspoons of chamomile flowers into one cup of hot water for ten to fifteen minutes.

2. Allow this to cool slightly and give it to your child to drink.

3. You can add raw honey to make it easier for your child to consume.

4. Pouring the tea into popsicle molds and having your child consume it this way may help relieve a headache better than drinking a warm beverage, so consider trying this when your child has a headache.

Other Ideas to Help Ease a Headache

In addition to the remedies above for headaches, you can help your child feel better by dimming the lights in the room, turning off all electronic screens (the blue light from screens can trigger headaches or make an existing headache worse), placing a hot or cold pack on the area, and giving her plenty of water to drink, to stay hydrated. Sometimes dehydration can also trigger headaches.

As parents, it can be stressful when we watch our children experience the aches and pains that come with living this life. Remember that, without pain, our children wouldn't understand or appreciate the beauty of feeling well and whole. They will get to see their parents demonstrating love and devotion to them, as they help them to feel better. These memories will likely stay with them for a lifetime.

Natural Cranberry Juice for Urinary Tract infections (UTIs)

Another issue that can occur commonly with children is a urinary tract infection. This infection happens because bacteria (most often pathogenic *E. coli*) get into the urinary tract, causing inflammation. According to the Urology Care Foundation, 2.5% of all children will suffer from a UTI at some point (Urology Care Foundation, 2016). Girls are much more likely than boys to get a UTI because a girl's urethra is shorter than a boy's. Symptoms of a UTI can include a sudden need to urinate, the need to urinate often, incontinence, pain or trouble urinating, blood in the urine, nausea or vomiting, fever or chills, tiredness, or irritability.

It is important to treat a UTI because the infection can spread to the kidneys, causing permanent damage. Steps to prevent UTIs include taking probiotics, not holding urine in the bladder, emptying out the bladder completely, and keeping proper hygiene. If your child is a girl, teach her to wipe herself from front to back, to lessen the likelihood of introducing bacteria into her urinary system. Cranberries are the most common natural treatment for a UTI, and 100% cranberry juice is most often utilized. Drinking lots of water is important to flush out the urinary tract, as well. Increasing vitamin C intake also helps because it strengthens your child's immune system. Of course, natural treatments are preferred but you should contact your doctor if new symptoms appear, if symptoms worsen or your child is not better within two to three days.

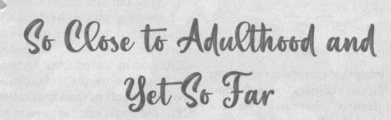

So Close to Adulthood and Yet So Far

(Ten Years Old and Beyond)

This is the part of raising children that every parent fears – adolescence! Is it really something to fear though? Sure, children at this stage are growing and changing into the adults they were meant to be. They are trying to sort out all the strange new feelings and emotions that come with fluctuating hormones. Their social life comes into the spotlight more, and it may feel like their friends take precedence over their parents during this phase. But at the end of the day, they will always be our children. They will get through this phase and come out on the other side with more appreciation and love for everything you have done for them! During this phase, hormones can cause issues ranging from acne to anxiety. The first menstrual period is likely to come during this phase as well. In this chapter, you will learn how to treat hormone-related issues such as menstrual issues, anxiety, and acne.

My mom was ten years old when she got her first menstrual period. She said she told her mom about it and she was simply handed a pad and showed how to use it. No explanation was given about what was happening or reassurance that this was a normal part of growing up. My mother developed severe endometriosis and experienced excruciating pain. Her

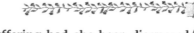

pain was so great that each month she was taken to the doctor to receive an injection of pain medication to help with her pain. Due to my mom's experiences as a child and adolescent she made sure to do a better job explaining these changes to her daughters, so we were prepared. She also made sure we were healthy and watched for any signs of hormonal imbalance.

We were quite young when our mother explained to us what a menstrual cycle was, how the body worked, and why it worked this way. Explaining how the body works, in an in-depth way, is a very enlightening and refreshing way to help your child experience adolescence and be ready for what is to come. Communicate and educate your child about his or her reproductive system, about ovulation, menstruation, sperm production and everything that comes with this phase of development. I am shocked at all the young adults today, both male and female, who have no idea about how their body works. We can do better for our children!

Menstrual cycles aren't exactly a walk in the park. Some women experience painful cramping, heavy blood loss, and mood swings. While cramping is normal to a degree, pay attention to your child's complaints and see a gynecologist to rule out anything serious if she is experiencing severe cramping. In the case of my mother, it wasn't until much later that she was diagnosed with endometriosis and by this point, there was scar tissue covering her reproductive organs, colon, and other areas. In the end she required laser surgery in order to have a chance to get pregnant later in life. She may have been saved from some of

her suffering had she been diagnosed earlier in life. For normal cramping, try the remedies below to help your child find relief.

Cramp Bark Tea

Cramp bark (*Viburnum opulus*) is excellent for helping to relax uterine tissues. It works great for relieving cramps and uterine spasms that cause pain and discomfort during menstruation.

1. You can create a tea with two teaspoons of cramp bark and one cup of water by bringing this to a boil on the stove.

2. Once it boils, reduce the heat and allow this to simmer for fifteen minutes.

3. Carefully strain the liquid and allow it to cool enough to consume.

4. Adults can drink up to three cups of this daily, but start with one cup and see how this works for your adolescent. If you need to give another cup, several hours later, this is fine.

Red Raspberry Leaf Infusion to Support Uterine Health

Perhaps one of the most popular herbs for women, due to its uterine toning effects, is red raspberry. This plant makes a safe and beneficial tea for those who want to support uterine health and overall reproductive wellness. Some women claim it helps regulate menstrual cycles, lessen heavy periods, and reduce cramping as well. This is not due to any hormone-altering compounds in the leaves, but rather to the uterine toning effects of the leaves. This can be enjoyed between periods to support the uterus and healthy menstruation. In addition to the benefits already mentioned, red raspberry leaf is full of antioxidants, potassium, and other vitamins and minerals that our bodies need to thrive.

1. Create a drink using the nourishing infusion protocol by infusing one cup of the dried leaves in one quart of water.

2. Drink two cups daily for best results.

Yarrow Tea for Heavy Bleeding

Losing more than 80 ml of blood during a menstrual cycle is considered heavy bleeding. If your adolescent is experiencing heavy blood loss during a menstrual cycle, she needs to see a gynecologist to make sure everything is okay. In the meantime, if you are concerned with blood loss during menstruation, it can also help staunch internal bleeding.

1. Create a gentle tea with yarrow by infusing one to two teaspoons of yarrow in one cup of hot water for ten to fifteen minutes.

2. Drink one to two cups daily as needed, for supporting healthy menstrual flow.

Anxiety and Mood Swings

Fluctuating hormones can play with one's emotional state. This is especially true for anyone going through puberty. The effects of hormones can manifest themselves in anxiety and mood swings for both males and females. There are several effective herbal remedies that can help to uplift and stabilize the mood naturally, without the use of harmful chemicals. Below are some wonderful nervine remedies you can use to help your adolescent when he or she is feeling overwhelmed or anxious.

California Poppy Tea

Is your adolescent feeling anxious or stressed? California poppy (*Eschscholzia*

californica) tea may help him calm down and relax. It is a gentle sedative that helps to promote relaxation in those with nervous agitation. It is also used to help with insomnia and for those who need nervous system support. It is gentle enough to use with children and adults alike.

1. Infuse one to two teaspoons of California poppy into one cup of hot water and allow this to infuse for ten to fifteen minutes before consuming.

2. Drink up to three cups daily as needed for anxiety and stress.

Motherwort Anti-stress Tea

For those who are feeling overwhelmed, motherwort (*Leonurus cardiaca*) can come to the rescue. This lovely member of the mint family helps reduce tension and stress, especially when this is triggered by hormonal issues. Motherwort is also a valuable herb for those seeking mood swing stabilization. It makes a fine companion for anyone suffering from hormone–related anxiety and the feeling of being overwhelmed. It gently calms the body and may also help support a healthy heart.

1. Infuse one to two teaspoons of this herb in a cup of hot water for ten to fifteen minutes.

2. Drink one to two cups as needed, for mood swings, anxiety, and tension.

Skullcap and Lemon Balm Tea

Do frazzled nerves have your adolescent worked up? Does your child seem to blow up at every little thing? Skullcap and lemon balm (*Melissa officinalis*) tea may be just what she needs to recover and become more grounded. Historically, skullcap has been given to those suffering from "insanity," but this member of the mint family has a lot more to offer. It is a gentle nervine that works especially well for those who seem to be on edge. Lemon balm is a safe and gentle herb that helps to calm as well. It pairs amazingly well with skullcap in a tea for frazzled nerves.

1. Infuse one teaspoon of each herb into one cup of hot water for ten to fifteen minutes.

2. Drink one to two cups of this tea as needed, to calm the nerves.

Acne

For me, acne was more of a problem than mood swings or menstrual issues during adolescence. Not everyone will understand this, but those with acne will … Acne doesn't just alter a person physically, it can have traumatic mental and emotional effects. Some lucky adolescents will go through this phase with hardly a blemish, while others can come out of the phase permanently scarred. After half a lifetime of acne, I have learned a great deal about how to control breakouts and treat those pesky zits. Below are some of the most effective remedies I have found that help with treating acne.

We are What We Eat

Your adolescent is probably not going to want to hear this, but food is a huge trigger for acne. I highly recommend eliminating certain foods for a month to see if this makes a difference. First: dairy. Dairy seems to be a big culprit behind acne for many people. Cut the milk, cheeses, and other dairy products for a while to see if you notice any difference. If your adolescent is a big milk drinker, substitute almond milk or coconut milk for dairy milk. Have him or her keep a food journal as well, in which the food eaten each day is documented, along with an assessment of acne breakouts from week to week. Describe the severity of the acne – is it mild, moderate, or severe? In addition

to dairy, try eliminating sugar, gluten, and caffeine. The less processed foods they eat, the better. I never failed to notice clearer skin when I was eating a healthy diet rich in vegetables, fruits, and lean meats.

Aloe and Tea Tree Spot Treatment

Aloe vera is naturally anti-inflammatory and helps tremendously to reduce redness and inflammation caused by acne. In addition, it is antimicrobial so it can help kill the bacteria that cause acne. Tea tree (*Melaleuca alternifolia*) is an excellent acne treatment too, because of its strong, yet skin-nourishing antibacterial properties. When combined, these two plant-derived ingredients create an acne-fighting powerhouse.

1. Blend three drops of tea tree essential oil with one tablespoon of food grade aloe vera gel in a small sterile bowl.

2. Apply this to acne in the morning and evening (after cleaning the face with warm water and soap).

3. For severe acne, apply a small amount all over a clean face (avoid the eyes and mucous membranes), twice daily.

Dandelion Root Tea

Dandelions are such a common sight that many people don't realize they are a medicinal treasure. They are one of my, and our local pollinators', favorite flowers. My children called them 'wish flowers' when they were little because of the tradition of blowing off their seeds while making a wish. All parts

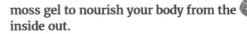

of the dandelion have a use, with the leaves and flowers being edible and the taproot possessing medicinal qualities. Dandelion root is known for its tonic effect on the body. It helps to flush out toxins and purify the blood. As a result, it can flush out impurities that may be causing acne.

1. Infuse one to two teaspoons of chopped dandelion root into one cup of hot water.

2. Drink this daily for clearer skin.

Sea Moss Skin Gel

Is there anything sea moss (*Chondrus crispus*) cannot do? Probably, but it sure has a myriad of uses! Sea moss has exploded in popularity in the past few years, and for good reason. It contains many vitamins, minerals, and nutrients that benefit the body when used internally and externally. It is cooling, soothing, and healing to the skin. It has potent antioxidant, anti-inflammatory, and antimicrobial properties, making it especially useful for treating acne. You can create a sea moss gel to nourish your body from the inside out.

1. Purchase dried sea moss from a reputable vendor (Join to our FB group, link at the end, and check out the Saturday post for vendors, or ask where to find them).

2. Rinse a small amount of the sea moss and soak it in a bowl of water overnight.

3. The next day, remove the sea moss from the water (it will have expanded and enlarged) and place it in a blender.

4. Add a small amount of fresh water and run the blender.

5. Add more water as needed, to reach a gel-like consistency.

6. When you have the consistency you desire, pour your sea moss gel into a sterile glass jar and refrigerate it.

7. It should last three to four weeks if refrigerated.

8. To use, simply apply a liberal amount to the skin, twice daily (morning and evening), and rinse it off after twenty minutes, using warm water and a cloth.

9. You can also add a tablespoon to a nutrition drink or shake each day for much-needed vitamins, minerals, and nutrients that may help to cleanse and purify the body.

Apple Cider Vinegar and Tea Tree Oil for Ringworm

Another unsightly and unpleasant thing you and your child may encounter is a tinea infection (sometimes also known as ringworm or athlete's foot). These infections aren't actually caused by a worm but rather by a fungus that infects various locations on the body. According to Johns Hopkins Medicine, "Tinea infections on the scalp, arms, legs, face, and trunk are characterized by ring-shaped, red, scaly patches with clearing centers. Tinea infections of the feet, nails, and genital areas are not generally referred to as ringworm, as they may not take on the typical ring shape"(Johns Hopkins Medicine, Undated). Treatment from the doctor most often involves the use of an antifungal cream but can also include a special shampoo if the infection is on the scalp, or oral antifungal medicine for scalp or nail infections as they are the hardest to treat. There are some home remedies, including applying apple cider vinegar and tea tree oil three times daily, or making a paste or salve from black walnut hulls (follow previous instructions on salve making) and applying it. These infections will spread so if there is no improvement within a few days, see a doctor for further treatment.

Adolescence is a time of great change. By the end of this phase, the little child you once knew will be all grown up into the adult you helped mold with love and integrity. Your son or daughter may someday have the chance to pass on all the wisdom you demonstrated with your herbal remedies, and your grandchildren will get the same love and care that you gave your child! Herbal remedies aren't just a way to achieve wellness; they are a legacy you can leave for generations to come.

The Guardian Angel's Thankless Job

(∞)

Did you think we'd forget you? Being a parent is a thankless job, but we know that you are the person who spent many sleepless nights caring for your child with all the love you have to give. Not only can you have a healthier child by educating yourself on herbal remedies, you will also have resources to care for yourself. Below are herbal remedies you can use to stay strong, physically and mentally, because raising children isn't for the faint of heart!

When my sister had her fourth child, she reached out to me. Things were getting overwhelming. She had two children that were only one year apart in age. When she brought her newborn home, she had a one year old, a three year old, and a five year old waiting for their mom as well. I was really honored that she reached out, because not all moms want to talk about the overwhelming anxiety that sometimes creeps in during the postpartum phase. My sister came to me asking what she could do to feel better, naturally, and get rid of the dark cloud that seemed to follow her. First, I told her that herbal remedies aren't always the first thing I reach for when I am feeling that way. They are extremely effective and useful, but some moms need help in the form of a BREAK.

I came over and did laundry, brought food, and watched her kids while she took a shower and had some time alone to herself. Friends, this made all the difference. Sometimes a mom just needs a shower and time to do her hair in order to feel "whole" again. Keep this in mind if you have a friend who is a new mom (or dad). Offer your support, be present for her (or him). You have no idea just how important your actions can be! In addition to giving my dear sister a much-needed break, I brought a few herbal remedies for her to use. Below are some remedies to help a new mom find peace and balance as she navigates motherhood.

Motherwort Tincture for Mother Care

Motherwort got its name for its ability to nourish and care for mothers. The name actually dates back to the time of the early Greeks, when this plant was used for pregnant mothers who were suffering from anxiety. It is certainly a woman's best friend. In moderate doses, motherwort is safe for breastfeeding women. A little really goes a long way. I suggested my sister take five drops of motherwort tincture in a glass of water, as needed, when she was feeling overwhelmed. She called me one day and told me she has never taken anything that has helped her as much as the motherwort I gave her. To

this day, she keeps it on hand for its gentle, calming effects.

Skullcap Nervine Tincture

Skullcap is an excellent nervine, and can help to calm frazzled nerves. If you find yourself sensitive to even the smallest things, this can be a sign you are on edge and need a break. Take a step back and reset with skullcap tincture. Try taking one to two droppers full under the tongue, up to twice daily, to soothe the nerves.

Passionflower Pre-Bedtime Tincture

If you are a mom who has trouble getting to sleep because your mind won't quit racing, passionflower (*Passiflora incarnata*) may be just what you need. Not only is passionflower an excellent herb for helping one get to sleep, it can also help relieve anxiety and stress. Take one to two droppers full of passionflower tincture around one hour before bedtime to help quiet the mind in preparation for a good night's sleep.

Valerian Root Tincture for Relaxation

If you need a heavy hitter for insomnia, valerian root can help. Valerian root is one of the most potent herbs for insomnia, anxiety, and stress. It is a mild Central Nervous System (CNS) depressant, meaning it can slow things down to help you wind down and relax. Do not take valerian during the daytime, as it will likely make you drowsy. In addition, avoid taking this remedy if you plan to operate heavy machinery or drive a car. The best time to take valerian root tincture is one hour before bedtime. From experience, I add that this remedy didn't cause a deep enough sleep that my baby couldn't wake me up when she needed to nurse. Take one to two droppers full under the tongue. This particular tincture has an undesirable flavor for some people, and if you happen to dislike it, you can add the tincture to a glass of water and take it this way.

Hops Anxiety Tincture

If you thought hops (*Humulus lupulus*) were just for making beer, you would be wrong! Hops are a really effective sedative and nervine remedy that works to ease anxiety and reduce stress. This alkaline plant helps to modulate GABA receptors in the brain, making it useful for those in need of upliftment and peace. Hops are a great remedy for those who need the occasional boost to help them through the day. They are not a remedy I would suggest taking daily, but they are good every now and then, as needed. Take one to two droppers full of this tincture when you are feeling nervous, anxious, or overwhelmed.

Conclusion

(A Network of Love)

When my firstborn son was laid in my arms for the first time I looked into his eyes and knew right then that I was going to do everything I could to ensure he had the best. This came from an instinct deep down inside of me; I just knew that there was another way. I knew that I could do better for him. Using herbs was one of the cornerstones of this love-driven quest for my family. I spent years researching, using trial and error, and delving deeply into herbal education to learn what I know today. And the catalyst for this quest was my children. This book contains my most effective remedies. It delivers nearly everything a parent would need to know in order to raise a truly healthy child. I am delighted to be able to share these remedies with others so they have the chance to lay a firm foundation of wellness for their families.

Through this book, you have had the opportunity to learn about herbal remedies, as well as how to use many common herbs to create simple yet effective treatments for a variety of issues as they arise. From the first moments to the first weeks and months, this book has delivered everything I have learned and everything I wish I had known when I first had children of my own. I decided to outline the various phases of a child's life, from infancy and throughout childhood to adolescence, so parents could have resources as they need them to deal with life's challenges.

If there is one thing I want readers to take away from this book, it is this: You are capable, you are worthy. You are called to be the parent of your child and you have what it takes to step up in this calling and be the best parent you can be. This book will give you what you need to do the job!

The remedies above are just a few you can employ when you need help. There are many other remedies available. A great resource to have is my book *The Art of Herbal Healing: Herbalism for Beginners* which will help you to learn more about useful herbal remedies for adults and children alike! I also wrote a book about how to grow your own herbs, my second ever book; *Grow Your Own Medicine: Handbook for the Self-Sufficient Herbalist*. You may find these books interesting to improve your overall knowledge about growing and using herbs.

Remember, having a network of people willing to help you can make

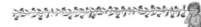

a huge difference when parenting children of any age. I will never forget the look on my sister's face and her appreciation when I came over to help with her family. There is an old saying that it takes a village to raise a child, and this is true for my family. We are all there for each other and help each other when we see signs of struggle. We share herbal remedies and help each other plant herb gardens each spring.

My sister and I watch each other's children so we can each have a break. This is the definition of love! Be there for the ones you love and if possible, have a network of support so you can have some help along the way on this amazing journey! You are not alone! There are networks of parents just like you – reach out to them.

Share your progress with your friends and with your fellow herbal companions in our Facebook group. Share your progress with your friends and with your fellow herbal companions in our Facebook group. You can find the **LINK and QR code to join in resources at the end.**

Once you have educated yourself on the herbal remedies in this book, what next? There is a great big world out there with so much more to learn! Look for more books to come.

Now that you have access to the beneficial herbal remedies in this book that make parenthood (and childhood) a bit easier, why not share the love? We encourage you to help other parents out! Introduce others to the world of herbal remedies by giving this book to three other people. You could be doing them a huge service by making their lives easier, as well as helping them feel more empowered to care for their little ones.

Pass on the love.

A small favor

Did you learn a thing or two and enjoyed this book?
Please consider scanning the QR code below to leave a short review.
These reviews cure my aching author heart.

It won't take longer than 30 seconds. It can be just a sentence or
two. Thank you, it means alot to me.

Or send an email to "Adrian@greenhopex.com" with subject "Raised
Naturally Review" and I will send you the review link <3

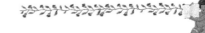

Resources

See The Art of Herbal healing and other books by Ava

www.theherb.space/books

Join our private FB group

www.theherb.space/group

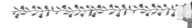

References and Resources

Adams, K. M., Lindell, K. C., Kohlmeier, M., & Zeisel, S. H. (2006). Status of nutrition education in medical schools. The American journal of clinical nutrition, 83(4), 941S–944S. https://doi.org/10.1093/ajcn/83.4.941S

Centers for Disease Control and Prevention. (2020). Parasites: Children. Centers for Disease Control and Prevention. https://www.cdc.gov/parasites/children.html

Choi, A. L., Guifan, S., Zhang, Y., & Grandjean, P. 2012. Developmental fluoride neurotoxicity: a systematic review and meta-analysis. Environmental Health Perspectives, 120 (10), https://ehp.niehs.nih.gov/doi/10.1289/ehp.1104912

Garone, S. (2020). Are vegan babies and toddlers at risk for health problems? Healthline. https://www.healthline.com/health/baby/vegan-baby

Herbal Academy. (2021). How to make rolled herb pills. Herbal Academy; International School of Herbal Arts and Sciences. https://theherbalacademy.com/rolled-herb-pills-video/

Hinde, S., & Fairchild, R. (2018). Why vegan diets for babies come with significant risks. The Conversation. https://theconversation.com/amp/why-vegan-diets-for-babies-come-with-significant-risks--108466

Johns Hopkins Medicine. (Undated). Tinea infections (Ringworm). Johns Hopkins Medicine; Health. https://www.hopkinsmedicine.org/health/conditions-and-diseases/tinea-infections-ringworm#:~:text=It%20happens%20mainly%20in%20children,It%20rarely%20happens%20in%20adults

Kuratko, C. N., Barrett, E. C., Nelson, E. B., & Salem, N., Jr (2013). The relationship of docosahexaenoic acid (DHA) with learning and behavior in healthy children: a review. Nutrients, 5(7), 2777–2810. https://pubmed.ncbi.nlm.nih.gov/23877090/

Kuzemchak, S. (2021). Everything you need to know about heavy metals and contaminants in baby food. Parents.com. https://www.parents.com/recipes/scoop-on-food/clean-label-project-study-finds-contaminants-in-formula-baby-food/

Lakshmi, Dr., Geetha, R. V., Roy, A., & Subramanian, A. K. (2011). Yarrow (Achillea millefolium Linn.), a herbal medicinal plant with broad therapeutic use - A review. International Journal of Pharmaceutical Sciences Review and Research, 9, pg. 136-141.

Rudloff, S., Bührer, C., Jochum, F. et al. (2019). Vegetarian diets in childhood and adolescence. Mol Cell Pediatr 6, 4. https://molcellped.springeropen.com/articles/10.1186/s40348-019-0091-z#Abs1

Sutter, D. O., & Bender, N. (2021). Nutrient status and growth in vegan children. Nutrition Research 21, 13–25. https://www.sciencedirect.com/science/article/pii/S0271531721000191

Urology Care Foundation. (2016). Understanding UTIs across the lifespan. Urology Care Foundation: The official foundation of the American Urological Association. https://www.urologyhealth.org/healthy-living/urologyhealth-extra/magazine-archives/summer-2016/understanding-utis-across-the-lifespan

Zimlich, R. (2017). Herbs are helpful, but use with caution in children. Contemporary pediatrics. https://www.contemporarypediatrics.com/view/herbs-are-helpful-use-caution-children